1948

The Terry Lectures

ON UNDERSTANDING SCIENCE
An Historical Approach

ON UNDERSTANDING SCIENCE

An Historical Approach

BY

JAMES B. CONANT

PRESIDENT OF HARVARD UNIVERSITY

NEW HAVEN

YALE UNIVERSITY PRESS

LONDON · GEOFFREY CUMBERLEGE · OXFORD UNIVERSITY PRESS

1947

THE DWIGHT HARRINGTON TERRY FOUNDATION

LECTURES ON RELIGION IN THE LIGHT OF SCIENCE AND PHILOSOPHY

THIS volume is based upon the twenty-third series of lectures delivered at Yale University on the Foundation established by the late Dwight H. Terry of Bridgeport, Connecticut, through his gift of $100,000 as an endowment fund for the delivery and subsequent publication of "Lectures on Religion in the Light of Science and Philosophy."

The deed of gift declares that "the object of this Foundation is not the promotion of scientific investigation and discovery, but rather the assimilation and interpretation of that which has been or shall be hereafter discovered, and its application to human welfare, especially by the building of the truths of science and philosophy into the structure of a broadened and purified religion. The founder believes that such a religion will greatly stimulate intelligent effort for the improvement of human conditions and the advancement of the race in strength and excellence of character. To this end it is desired that lectures or a series of lectures be given by men eminent in their respective departments, on ethics, the history of civilization and religion, biblical research, all sciences and branches of knowledge which have an important bearing on the subject, all the great laws of nature, especially of evolution . . . also such interpretations of literature and sociology as are in accord with the spirit of this Foundation, to the end that the Christian spirit may be nurtured in the fullest light of the world's knowledge and that mankind may be helped to attain its highest possible welfare and happiness upon this earth . . .

"The lectures shall be subject to no philosophical or religious test and no one who is an earnest seeker after truth shall be excluded because his views seem radical or destructive of existing beliefs. The founder realizes that the liberalism of one generation is often conservatism in the next, and that many an apostle of true liberty has suffered martyrdom at the hands of the orthodox. He therefore lays special emphasis on complete freedom of utterance, and would welcome expressions of conviction from sincere thinkers of differing standpoints even when these may run counter to the generally accepted views of the day. The founder stipulates only that the managers of the fund shall be satisfied that the lecturers are well qualified for their work and are in harmony with the cardinal principles of the Foundation, which are loyalty to the truth, lead where it will, and devotion to human welfare."

CONTENTS

ILLUSTRATIONS

Preface

TO WRITE a book about science in the year 1946 without some consideration of the atomic bomb may seem the academic equivalent of fiddling while Rome burns. For all intelligent citizens must place the international control of atomic energy at the top of any list of urgent matters. Anything that any individual or group of individuals can do to forward the solution of the international problem has obviously top priority. But as this year draws to a close, it appears that for the time being there is little that can be done by private citizens. The United States Government took the initiative in the formation of the United Nations Atomic Energy Commission. At the first meeting of the Commission the American representative put forward a carefully prepared plan for the effective international control of atomic energy. The whole problem is now being considered by the International Commission and the delicate negotiations will necessarily be slow. Until the United Nations Commission renders an official report, we must be patient—patient and courageous, for the prospects are grim, indeed, if the Commission should ultimately fail to reach agreement.

Yet, the American public has to learn to live with this problem of the atomic bomb. The natural tendency of many people to recoil with horror from all thoughts of further scientific advance because of the implications of the atomic bomb is to my mind based on a misapprehension of the nature of the universe. As I watched the secret development of the atomic bomb through four years of war, I often thought of the work being done at the same time under the auspices of the Medical Research Committee. I knew of the then secret research on penicillin, on DDT, on anti-malarial drugs, on the use of blood plasma, and realized how much these scientific advances meant for the future welfare of mankind. As I contrasted the development of the atomic bomb and the medical investigations, I often thought of Emerson's famous essay on the Law of Compensation.

In the early days of the work on atomic energy there was a possibility that the constants of nature would be such that atomic energy for power would be possible, but an atomic explosive impossible. We all hoped this would be the case, though the probabilities were slight. In fact, I often thought in that uncertain period that this would be too good to be true—the universe just isn't built that way. So it turned out in fact. Science and its applications have given us marvelous drugs and ways of health, communications, transportation, luxuries of every sort; it has also given us the atomic bomb, the discovery of which was in a sense inevitable in a scientific age—only the timing was uncertain. And I believe history will record that the democracies were very fortunate in the timing.

As Emerson has written, ". . . Every excess causes a defect; every defect an excess. . . . Every faculty which is a receiver of pleasure has an equal penalty put on its abuse. . . . With every influx of light comes new danger. . . . There is a crack in everything God has made. It would seem there is always this vindictive circumstance stealing in at unawares . . . this back-stroke, this kick of the gun, certifying that the law is fatal; that in nature nothing can be given, all things are sold."

If, following Emerson, we think of the potential power of destruction of the atomic bomb as the price we pay for health and comfort and aids to learning in this scientific age, we can perhaps more coolly face the task of making the best of an inevitable bargain, however hard. Remembering that Emerson warned that "the doctrine of compensation is not the doctrine of indifference," we can begin to walk boldly along the tightrope of the atomic age.

It is with such thoughts in mind that I venture in the following pages to discuss science as neither a benign nor a malignant activity of man, but as a process of unveiling many things, all of which have "cracks." Whether we have courage enough to face the most recent evidence of this "fatal law" and intelligence enough to proceed with the next stage in the development of civilization will in part depend on education. This fact in itself would be justification enough for all of us who spend our lives trying to explore new and better ways of "perpetuating learning to posterity."

A few words of warning are perhaps in order to those readers who as teachers may be interested in the point of view presented. No attempt has been made to present the material in the form of a manual for instructors. I have had to content myself with general suggestions on the one hand, and a few incomplete illustrations on the other. I have presented neither a syllabus for a college course nor even the details of any single case history. Lack of time and ignorance I must plead as my twin excuses for the many shortcomings of this small book. But even if someone much more learned in the history of science than I were to devote his entire energies to the development of a course of the type I am suggesting, progress would be slow. The greatest hindrance to the widespread use of case histories in teaching science is the lack of suitable case material. Limitations in this regard would virtually require the instructor to choose his topics quite as much because of the availability of printed material as because of their intrinsic pedagogic value.

I am hopeful that if a sufficient number of teachers become interested in the approach suggested in the following pages, a coöperative enterprise might be launched which would go far to overcome the difficulties now presented by the paucity of printed material available for student use. The professional students of the history of science and those engaged in the teaching of science as part of a general education (at the college level) might well join forces. Together they might plan for the translation, editing, and publishing in suitable form of extracts from the history of science which would be of importance to the college teacher. It is no small undertaking, but one of the first importance. When it is remembered that two of the most significant works in the history of science, the *De revolutionibus* of Copernicus and the *De fabrica* of Vesalius, have never been published in English translation —to say nothing of the vast amount of untranslated writings of Kepler, Galileo, Lavoisier, Galvani, and a host of others—it is evident how much remains to be accomplished. At present the choice of reading assignments in English for students, quite apart from the availability of the books, is very limited. But even within the narrow limits thus imposed, a start could be made. And from such beginnings sufficient interest might be awakened in the academic world to make possible the further scholarly work of translating and editing which would provide an expanding foundation for those engaged in the collegiate teaching of general science.

The bibliographies given in the Appendix of the present volume may prove helpful to any who might be interested in developing the case histories I have suggested.

They have been prepared by Mr. I. B. Cohen of Harvard. I am deeply indebted to him not only for this assistance but for his collaboration in assembling the historical material on which my case histories are based. Without his knowledge of the history of science, his fruitful suggestions, and his help in preparing the manuscript for publication it would have been literally impossible for me to present my ideas about teaching science in their present form.

It is a pleasure to express my gratitude to the authorities of Yale University for the invitation to deliver the Terry Lectures on the general topic of an historical approach to science. Without this stimulation I should hardly have found either the time or the courage to formulate in a public document certain thoughts about teaching science which have been forming in my mind for many years.

JAMES B. CONANT

November 20, 1946.

ON UNDERSTANDING SCIENCE

CHAPTER I

The Scientific Education of the Layman

THIS book is concerned primarily with a simple yet difficult pedagogic problem. I propose to examine the question of how we can in our colleges give a better understanding of science to those of our graduates who are to be lawyers, writers, teachers, politicians, public servants, and businessmen. To the extent that my answer to this query has novelty, I shall be forced to illustrate by example. Since it is my contention that science can best be understood by laymen through close study of a few relatively simple case histories, I have no choice but to present some fragments of scientific history. This I shall do in the second and third chapters which are intended to convey certain ideas about the "Tactics and Strategy of Science." But first of all I should like to consider why any but a relatively few experts need to understand science, and then, to explain at some length what the phrase "understanding science" means to me.

Assimilating Science into Our Secular Culture

The three lectures on which this book is based were delivered at Yale University on the Terry Foundation. One of the objects of the Terry Foundation is "the assimilation of what has been or will be hereafter discovered, and its application to human welfare." I like the word "assimilation"; its use in connection with science at once brings to mind one of the unsolved problems of this age. Is it not because we have failed to assimilate science into our western culture that so many feel spiritually lost in the modern world? So it seems to me. Once an object has been assimilated, it is no longer alien; once an idea has been absorbed and incorporated into an integrated complex of ideas, the erstwhile foreign intruder becomes an element of strength. And in this process of assimilation, labels may well disappear. When what we now roughly designate as science has been fully assimilated into our cultural stream, we shall perhaps no longer use the word as we do today. When that time arrives, as I have no doubt it will, the subject of this book will be fused into the age-old problem of understanding man and his works: in short, secular education.

I use the words "secular education" advisedly. And in so doing I trust I shall not offend unduly either the faithful or the unbelieving. There will be some who feel that any attempt to carve off an area and designate it "secular education" is to destroy the basis for unity in our civilization, as well as to negate the very meaning of life. At the other extreme will be some among my friends who as militant antisupernaturalists will reject the adjective secular as being superfluous; they resent any implication that there may be indeed another realm of understanding. The existence of this wide gulf between men of good will, intelligence, and great learning is a fact of modern life. Those of us who are temperamentally the heretical Christians of each century must reckon with it, particularly when we discuss either science or education.

The evolution of a new culture appears to proceed in stages; at each stage there are topics which lend themselves to fruitful public discussion and vice versa. Today, even less than when the Terry Foundation was established, can one publicly examine with profit the special concern of the founder, namely, how "the truths of science and philosophy can be built into the structure of a broadened and purified religion." For the underlying premise of this statement is sure to be attacked in force from two opposing sides: the orthodox deny the validity of broadening or purifying their religion; those diametrically opposed deny the validity of all religions. Under such conditions intelligent interchange of views becomes difficult, to say the least. Perhaps the reforming protestants interested in philosophy and science would do well to bide their time. At all events, in discussing immediate educational matters they can obtain some coherence among men of divergent views by insisting on the significance of a discussion of the circumscribed field of secular learning.

My argument, therefore, runs as follows: we need a widespread understanding of science in this country, for only thus can science be assimilated into our secular cultural pattern. When that has been achieved, we shall be one step nearer the goal which we now desire so earnestly, a unified, coherent culture suitable for our American democracy in this new age of machines and experts.

Science and National Policy

There is another and more immediate reason for desiring a wider understanding of science in the United States. And if this reason is cogent, we should be concerned with pedagogic problems of adult education quite as much as with those at the college level. For the argument is a highly practical one related to issues now before the nation.

In a democracy, political power is widely diffused. National policy is determined by the interaction of forces generated and guided by hundreds of thousands if not millions of local leaders and men of influence. Eventually within the limits imposed by public opinion decisions of far-reaching importance are made by a relatively few. These men are almost accidentally thrown into positions of temporary power by the forces working throughout our benignly chaotic system of political democracy. Because of the fact that the applications of science play so important a part in our daily lives, matters of public policy are profoundly influenced by highly technical scientific considerations. Some understanding of science by those in positions of authority and responsibility as well as by those who shape opinion is therefore of importance for the national welfare.

Such a statement made a decade ago might have seemed a presumptuous claim on the part of scientists. Today, with the as yet unsolved riddle of international control of atomic energy hanging ominously above us, such a statement may seem so obvious as to require no elaboration. At all events, I shall not press the point further.

Concerning the Methods of Science

Up to this point I have used the word science as though it were synonymous with those fields of human activity often described as the natural sciences—physics, chemistry, astronomy, geology, and biology. To the average citizen it is the startling advances in these subjects that come to mind when one speaks of "pure science." Likewise, it is the application of the new knowledge in these areas to technology, to medicine, to agriculture, and, alas, to war that looms large in the public view when applied science is mentioned. Yet an increasing number of intelligent citizens believe that the social sciences rather than the physical or biological sciences hold the keys to the future. Others dissent violently from this view and even question the correctness of the phrase "social science."

One of the most significant discussions now in progress
turns on how far the methods by which the astonishing
results in pure and applied science have been achieved may
be transferred to other human activities. Among the questions on which learned and sincere men now disagree are
the following: Is there such a thing as a scientific method
of wide applicability in the solution of human problems?
Is there any significant difference between research in
basic science (or pure science) and in applied science? Are
the social sciences (psychology, anthropology, sociology,
political economy, economics, and history) really sciences?
If not, can they become so?

The answers to these and many related questions are of
supreme importance to the future of the free people. Our
educational procedures on the one hand and our collective
actions in regard to a variety of social, economic, and political problems on the other are all tangled up with this
current debate about the social sciences. Now, obviously, if
a layman is to have any clear ideas about the relation of
the methods of physics, chemistry, and biology to education or to the investigations of current issues, he must understand the methods in question. My third and final reason, therefore, for urging an improvement in the scientific
education of the layman rests on the need for clarification
of popular thinking about the methods of science. We need
to lay the basis for a better discussion of the ways in which
rational methods may be applied to the study and solution
of human problems.

Are All Rational and Impartial Inquiries Scientific?

One extreme position which has been maintained with
some insistence for the last seventy-five years attempts to
equate the scientific method with all relatively impartial
and rational inquiries. Somewhat more than fifty years
ago, for example, Karl Pearson in his *Grammar of Science*

proclaimed that "Modern science, as training the mind to an exact and impartial analysis of facts, is an education specially fitted to promote sound citizenship." And for the busy layman he recommended that, "What is necessary is the thorough knowledge of some small group of facts, the recognition of their relationship to each other, and of the formulae or laws which express scientifically their sequences. It is in this manner that the mind becomes imbued with the scientific method and freed from individual bias in the formation of its judgments—one of the conditions, as we have seen, for ideally good citizenship. This first claim of scientific training, its education in method, is to my mind the most powerful claim it has to state support."

I shall return later to Pearson's exposition of the scientific method; an exposition with which I find grave difficulties. For the moment I wish to concentrate attention only on two implications that run all through his introductory chapters: first, that an exact and impartial analysis of facts is alone possible in the realm of science; second, that exposure to such a discipline will produce a frame of mind that makes for impartial analysis in all matters.

Now, of course, there is no question that one of the necessary conditions for scientific investigation is an exact and impartial analysis of the facts. But this attitude was neither invented by those who first concerned themselves with scientific inquiries, nor was its overriding importance at once recognized. As one skims the histories of the natural sciences, it seems clear that in the embryonic stages of each of the modern disciplines, violent polemics rather than reasoned opinions often flowed most easily from the pen. This will be illustrated in more detail in the next two chapters. But if I read the history of science in the seventeenth and eighteenth centuries rightly, it was only gradually that there evolved the idea that a scientific investigator must impose on himself a rigorous self-discipline the moment he enters his laboratory. As each new generation saw how the prejudice and vanity of their predecessors proved stumbling blocks to progress, standards of exactness and impartiality were raised. But as long as science was largely a field for amateurs, as it was well into the nineteenth century, a man could regard his discoveries like so many fish. If he defended their size against all detractors, and in so doing their length increased, well, his opponent was a well-known liar, too.

The formation of the scientific societies, their growing importance, and the gradual building up of a professional feeling about science slowly changed the atmosphere. The example of the few giants who, beginning with Galileo, had well recognized the need for self control became the accepted standard. The man who was inclined to use the same weapons in "philosophical" as in political and theological debate gave way to the modern scientist who places little reliance on persuading his opponent with rhetoric or driving him from the field with invective. For his jury today is a large body of well-informed peers and to them he need only present exact and impartial facts with the minimum of emotion. I am referring to scientists who speak to scientists, of course. I leave aside the great popularizers of science like Huxley who are really educators. I am not, for the moment, discussing those writings which concern science but are of a metaphysical nature, nor those which aim toward the acceptance of a new or altered cosmology.

Would it be too much to say that in the natural sciences today the given social environment has made it very easy for even an emotionally unstable person to be exact and impartial in his laboratory? The traditions he inherits, his instruments, the high degree of specialization, the crowd of witnesses that surrounds him, so to speak (if he publishes his results)—these all exert pressures that make impartiality on matters of *his* science almost automatic. Let him deviate from the rigorous role of impartial experimenter or observer at his peril; he knows all too well what a fool So-and-so made of himself by blindly sticking to a set of observations or a theory now clearly recognized to be in error. But once he closes the laboratory door behind him, he can indulge his fancy all he pleases and perhaps with all the less restraint because he is now free from the imposed discipline of his calling. One would not be surprised, therefore, if as regards matters beyond their professional competence laboratory workers were a little less impartial and self-restrained than other men, though my own observations lead me to conclude that as human beings scientific investigators are statistically distributed over the whole spectrum of human folly and wisdom much as other men.

Who were the precursors of those early investigators who in the sixteenth and seventeenth centuries set the standards for exact and impartial scientific inquiries? Who were the spiritual ancestors of Copernicus, Galileo, and Vesalius? Not the casual experimenter or the artful contriver of new mechanical devices who gradually increased our empirical knowledge of physics and chemistry during the Middle Ages. These men passed on to subsequent generations many facts and valuable methods of attaining practical ends but not the spirit of scientific inquiry. For the burst of new ardor in disciplined intellectual inquiry we must turn to a few minds steeped in the Socratic tradition, and to those early scholars who first recaptured the culture of Greece and Rome by primitive methods of archaeology. In the first period of the Renaissance the love of dispassionate search for the truth was carried forward by those who were concerned with man and his works rather than with inanimate or animate nature. During the Middle Ages interest in attempts to use the human reason critically and without prejudice, to probe deeply without fear and favor, was kept alive more by those who wrote about human problems than about natural phenomena. In the early days of the Revival of Learning it was the humanist's exploration of antiquity that came nearest to exemplifying our modern ideas of impartial inquiry. Until the wave of scientific curiosity began to mount, inquiries into what we now call natural science were of little interest even to educated men. Scientific conclusions, unless they had profound influence on current cosmology, were apt to be lost like a pebble tossed into the sea.

Petrarch, Boccaccio, Machiavelli, and Erasmus, far more than the alchemists, must be considered the precursors of the modern scientific investigator. Likewise, Rabelais and Montaigne who carried forward the critical philosophic spirit must be counted, it seems to me, among the forerunners of the modern scientists. But not only a few hardy skeptics and the antiquarians, but also honest explorers and hardheaded statesmen and military commanders were the ancestors of all who endeavor to probe deeply to find new answers to old questions, who desire to minimize prejudice and examine facts impartially. As I see it, science today represents the accumulated fruits of one line of descent which migrated, so to speak, into certain fields which were ripe for cultivation. Once science became a self-propagating social phenomenon, those who till these fields have had a relatively easy time keeping up the tradition of their forebears.

Therefore, to put the scientist on a pedestal because he is an impartial inquirer is to misunderstand the situation entirely. Rather, if we seek to spread more widely among the population the desire to seek the facts without prej-

udice, we should pick our modern examples from the
nonscientific fields. We should examine and admire the
conduct of the relatively few who in the midst of human
affairs can courageously, honestly, and intelligently come
to conclusions based on reason without regard for their
own or other people's loyalties and interests, and having
come to these conclusions, can state them fairly, stick by
them, and act accordingly.

To say that all impartial and accurate analyses of facts
are examples of the scientific method is to add confusion
beyond measure to the problems of understanding science.
To claim that the study of science is the best education
for young men who aspire to become impartial analysts
of human affairs is to put forward a very dubious educational hypothesis at best. Indeed, those who contend that
the habits of thought and the point of view of the scientist
as a scientist can be transferred with advantage to other
human activities have hard work documenting their prop-
osition. Only an occasional brave man will be found nowadays to claim that the so-called scientific method is applicable to the solution of almost all the problems of daily
life in the modern world. Yet some proponents of this doctrine have at times gone even further and maintained that
only by a widespread application of the scientific method
to the problems of society at every level can we hope for
peace and sanity. Now, however, such extreme statements
are less likely to be coupled with an insistence on the dis-
ciplinary value of the physical sciences. One is more likely
to hear that what the layman needs is more education in
the social sciences.

With any idolatry of science I must confess I have little
sympathy. Yet a better understanding of natural science
among laymen might not be without value in developing
the attitude of which Karl Pearson spoke. Since scientific

investigations provide widespread and often dramatic examples of an effective way of handling problems, a greater knowledge of the genesis of scientific methods would probably reinforce certain habits of mind. Though the artificial restraints under which the experimentalist now operates unconsciously make cold-blooded factual analysis almost a routine operation, the demonstration day after day of the success of such methods is bound to have profound influence on public opinion. If properly understood, the demonstration strengthens those rational elements in our civic life which make for the adventurous yet orderly development of our free society. All of which is to say that a greater degree of understanding of science seems to me of importance for the welfare of the nation. But it is high time I proceeded to my task of suggesting how this may be achieved in fact.

Understanding Science

In my experience, a man who has been a successful investigator in any field of experimental science approaches a problem in pure or applied science, even in an area in which he is quite ignorant, with a special point of view. I designate this point of view "understanding science." Note carefully that it is independent of a knowledge of the scientific facts or techniques in the new area to which he comes. Even a highly educated and intelligent citizen without research experience will almost always fail to grasp the essentials in a discussion which takes place among scientists concerned with a projected inquiry. This will be so not because of the layman's lack of scientific knowledge or his failure to comprehend the technical jargon of the scientist; it will be to a large degree because of his fundamental ignorance of what science can or cannot accomplish, and his consequent bewilderment in the course of a discussion outlining a plan for a future investigation. He has no "feel" for the Tactics and Strategy of Science.

In the last five years I have seen repeated examples of such bewilderment of laymen. If I am right in this diagnosis (and it is the fundamental premise of this book), the remedy does not lie in a greater dissemination of scientific information among nonscientists. Being well informed about science is not the same thing as understanding science, though the two propositions are not antithetical. What is needed are methods for imparting some knowledge of the Tactics and Strategy of Science to those who are not scientists. Not that one can hope by any short-cut methods to produce in a layman's mind the same instinctive reaction toward scientific problems that is the hallmark of an investigator, but enough can be accomplished, I dare hope, to bridge the gap to some degree between those who understand science because science is their profession and those who have only studied the results of scientific inquiry—in short, the laymen.

But even if we agree that it is not more knowledge about science (more facts and principles) but some understanding of science that is required by the general public our pedagogic problem is not solved. For there are two ways of probing into complex human activities and their products: one is to retrace the steps by which certain end results have been produced, the other is to dissect the result with the hope of revealing its structural pattern and exposing the logical relations of the component parts, and, incidentally, exposing also the inconsistencies and flaws. Philosophic and mathematical minds prefer the logical approach, but it is my belief that for nine people out of ten the historical method will yield more real understanding of a complex matter.

For example, consider our form of government here in

the United States with its complicated interplay of state
and federal relations so baffling to even a highly educated
visitor from another democratic nation. In one sense, only
a few lawyers, statesmen, and political scientists understand the American Commonwealth. The rest of us can
find time only to try to obtain some understanding by the
study of a few books. Shall we follow Lord Bryce, for example, in looking for insight into the American constitu-
tion, or read Beard balanced by Charles Warren? For me,
the answer is easy; if I have to choose, the historian's story
will provide more understanding than the statesman's
analysis. Whether this is true for a large majority of students, only the teachers of political science and history
could say. But I venture the analogy to illustrate two
ways in which an understanding of science may be to some
degree attained by a relatively small amount of study.
You may turn to the philosopher's interpretation or you
may study examples of science in the making.

As far as the scientific education of the layman is concerned, I believe there is no real choice. It may be a toss-up
as to whether the political scientist or the historian can
give the better understanding of our government in a
limited amount of time; but the odds are all against the
philosopher, I believe, who has a parallel assignment in
regard to science. To be sure, he has had a clear field for
the most part, for the histories illustrating the Tactics
and Strategy of Science are as yet unwritten. But in spite
of this lack of competition I doubt if the philosophical
treatments of science and scientific method have been very
successful when viewed as an educational enterprise. No
one questions of course the importance of this type of
penetrating analysis. There must be constant critical ap-
praisal of the progress of science and in particular of
scientific concepts and operation. This is one of the prime

tasks of philosophers concerned with the unity of science and the problems of cosmology. But when learned discussions of these difficult matters are the sole source of popular knowledge about the ways of science, education in science may be more handicapped than helped by their wide circulation. I am inclined to think that, on the whole, the popularization of the philosophical analysis of science and its methods has led not to a greater understanding but to a great deal of misunderstanding about science.

To illustrate, let me once again refer to *The Grammar of Science*. Throughout the volume Karl Pearson refers to science as the classification of facts, and in his summary of the first chapter he writes as follows: "The scientific method is marked by the following features: (a) careful and accurate classification of facts and observation of their correlation and sequence; (b) the discovery of scientific laws by aid of the creative imagination; (c) self-criticism and the final touchstone of equal validity for all normally constituted minds." With (b) and (c) one can have little quarrel since all condensed statements of this are by necessity incomplete, but from (a) I dissent entirely. And it is the point of view expressed in this sentence that dominates Pearson's whole discussion. It seems to me, indeed, that one who had little or no direct experience with scientific investigations might be completely misled as to the nature of the scientific method by studying this famous book.

If science were as simple as this very readable account would have us believe, why did it take so long a period of fumbling before scientists were clear on some very familiar matters? Newton's famous work was complete by the close of the seventeenth century. The cultured gentlemen of France and England in the first decades of the eighteenth century talked in terms of a solar system almost identical with that taught in school today. The laws of motion and their application to mechanics were widely understood. Yet it was not until the 1770's that the common phenomenon of combustion was formulated in terms of comparable clarity; it was not until much later still that the concept of heat as a "mode of motion" was accepted. Spontaneous generation of life, you will recall, was an open question as late as the 1870's. Seventy-five years ago the Professor of Natural Philosophy at Harvard told his classes that "people now accept the undulatory theory of light because all those who formerly accepted the corpuscular theory are dead." The implied prophecy in this bit of skepticism turned out to be not far from the mark. Only within the lifetime of many of us has it been possible to develop concepts which take care of relatively simple facts concerning the emission and absorption of radiant energy. Darwin convinced himself and later the scientific world and later still the educated public of the correctness of the general idea of evolution because of a theory as to the mechanism by which evolution might have occurred. Today, the basic idea of the evolutionary development of higher plants and animals stands without question, but Darwin's mechanism has been so greatly questioned as to have been almost overthrown. And we are no nearer a solution of the problem of how life originated on this planet than we were in Darwin's day.

The stumbling way in which even the ablest of the early scientists had to fight through thickets of erroneous observations, misleading generalizations, inadequate formulations, and unconscious prejudice is the story which it seems to me needs telling. It is not told in courses in physics or chemistry or biology or any other of the natural sciences as far as I am aware. Take up a textbook of any of these subjects and see how very simple it all seems as far as method is concerned, and how very complicated the body of facts and principles soon becomes. Indeed, before you have got far in a freshman course you will find the harassed professor under pressure to be up to date bringing in subjects which cannot be adequately analyzed by the class at hand. Having insufficient knowledge of other disciplines, and particularly mathematics, the students have to take on faith statements about scientific laws and the structure of matter which are almost as dogmatic as though they were handed down by a high priest. Let me hasten to add, I am not blaming the teachers of these subjects. I have done the same in my time, and as an author of textbooks I am sinning in the same way today. For there is no other method of presenting factual knowledge in these subjects in this day of a vast interrelated and highly complicated fabric of physics, chemistry, and biology.

The Tactics and Strategy of Science

Let me now be specific as to my proposal for the reform of the scientific education of the layman. What I propose is the establishment of one or more courses at the college level on the Tactics and Strategy of Science. The objective would be to give a greater degree of understanding of science by the close study of a relatively few historical examples of the development of science. I suggest courses at the college level, for I do not believe they could be introduced earlier in a student's education; but there is no reason why they could not become important parts of programs of adult education. Indeed, such courses might well prove particularly suitable for older groups of men and women.

The analogy with the teaching of strategy and tactics

of war by examples from military history is obvious. And the success of that educational procedure is one reason why I venture to be hopeful about this new approach to understanding science. I also draw confidence from the knowledge of how the case method in law schools and a somewhat similar method in the Harvard Business School have demonstrated the value of this type of pedagogic device. The course would not aim to teach science—not even the basic principles or simplest facts—though as a by-product considerable knowledge of certain sciences would be sure to follow. Of course, some elementary knowledge of physics would be a prerequisite, but with the improvement in the teaching of science in high schools which is sure to come, this should prove no serious obstacle.

If one is content to give up the objectives of even a broad survey course—which are, to convey the basic facts and principles of science—one has a free hand in choosing the case histories. How they would in fact be chosen would depend on the inspiration of the teacher. All I can give in these lectures is one man's view, with the warning that it is based on no experience whatsoever with the type of teaching I suggest. Like many teachers of physics and chemistry and biology, I have from time to time quarried out bits from the history of a special science to assist my exposition. I have seen others go much further in the same direction with considerable success. But I must freely admit that what I am proposing represents a tremendous extrapolation from any educational experiments of which I am aware. Therefore, I warn that I may be peddling a rope of sand. But at all events, in so doing I shall have the satisfaction of answering for myself the question, "What is science?" not in analytical but in historic terms.

The case histories would almost all be chosen from the early days in the evolution of the modern discipline. Certain aspects of physics in the seventeenth and eighteenth centuries; chemistry in the eighteenth and nineteenth; geology in the early nineteenth; certain phases of biology in the eighteenth; others in the nineteenth. The advantages of this method of approach are twofold: first, relatively little factual knowledge is required either as regards the science in question or other sciences, and relatively little mathematics; second, in the early days one sees in clearest light the necessary fumblings of even intellectual giants when they are also pioneers; one comes to understand what science is by seeing how difficult it is in fact to carry out glib scientific precepts.

A few words may be in order as to the principles which would guide me in selecting case histories for my hypothetical course in the Tactics and Strategy of Science. I should wish to show the difficulties which attend each new push forward in the advance of science, and the importance of new techniques: how they arise, are improved, and often revolutionize a field of inquiry. I should hope to illustrate the intricate interplay between experiment, or observation, and the development of new concepts and new generalizations; in short, how new concepts evolve from experiments, how one conceptual scheme for a time is adequate and then is modified or displaced by another. I should want also to illustrate the interconnection between science and society about which so much has been said in recent years by our Marxist friends. I should have very little to say about the classification of facts, unless it were to use this phrase as a straw man. But I should hope that almost all examples chosen would show the hazards which nature puts in the way of those who would examine the facts impartially and classify them accurately. The "controlled experiment" and the planned or controlled observation would be in the forefront of every discussion. The difference in methods between the observational sciences of astronomy, geology, systematic biology on the one hand, and the experimental sciences of physics, chemistry, and experimental biology on the other should be emphasized.

To what extent a course in the Tactics and Strategy of Science should take cognizance of the existence of problems in metaphysics and epistemology would depend on the outlook of the instructor and the maturity and interest of the student. Obviously the course in question would not be one on the metaphysical foundations of modern science; yet the teacher can hardly ignore completely the influence of new scientific concepts on contemporary thinking about the structure of the universe or the nature and destiny of man. Nor can one fail in all honesty to identify at least vaguely those philosophic problems which have arisen when man has sought to examine critically the basis of his knowledge about "the external world." Perhaps in collaboration with a colleague from the department of philosophy the instructor would wish to suggest the reading of extracts from the writings of certain philosophers. If so, the existence of more than one school of thought should certainly be emphasized.

As I shall show in subsequent chapters, a discussion of the evolution of new conceptual schemes as a result of experimentation would occupy a central position in the exposition. This being so, there would be no escape from a consideration of the difficulties which historically have attended the development of new concepts. Is a vacuum really empty, if so, how can we see through it? Is action at a distance imaginable? These questions at one time in the forefront of scientific discussion are well worthy of careful review. The Newtonian theory of gravitation once disturbed "almost all investigators of nature because it was founded on an uncommon unintelligibility." It no longer disturbs us because "it has become a common unintelligibility." To what extent can the same statement be made about other concepts which have played a major part in the development of modern science? When we say that the chemists have "established" that chlorophyll is essential for photosynthesis and that they also have "established" the spatial arrangements of the carbon, hydrogen, and oxygen atoms in cane sugar, are we using the word "establish" in two different senses? These and similar questions should be explored in sufficient degree to make the student aware of some of the complexities which lie hidden behind our usual simplified exposition of the basic ideas of modern science in an elementary course.

However, I cannot emphasize too often that the course in question must *not* be concerned with the fruits of scientific inquiries, either as embodied in scientific laws or theories or cosmologies, or in the applications of science to industry or agriculture or medicine. Rather, the instructor would center his attention on the ways in which these fruits have been attained. One might call it a course in "scientific method" as illustrated by examples from history, except that I am reluctant to use this ambiguous phrase. I should prefer to speak of the methods by which science has been advanced, or perhaps we should say knowledge has been advanced, harking back to Francis Bacon's famous phrase, the advancement of learning.

Accumulative Knowledge, Philosophy, and Poetry

A certain degree of unity can be achieved in the learned world by emphasizing the fact that knowledge has indeed advanced in many areas in the last three hundred years. From this point of view alone there would be great advantages in having the case histories chosen from as many fields as possible. I have suggested on another occasion

that one may group together under the heading "accumulative knowledge" subjects as diverse as mathematics,
physics, chemistry, biology, anthropology, philology, and
archaeology. One can state with assurance that great advances have been made in these subjects in the last three
centuries. A similar statement cannot be made about philosophy, poetry, and the fine arts. If you are inclined to
doubt this and raise the question of how progress even in
academic matters can be defined, I would respond by ask-
ing you to perform an imaginary operation. Bring back
to life the great figures of the past who were identified with
the subjects in question. Ask them to view the present
scene and answer whether or not in their opinion there has
been an advance. No one can doubt how Galileo, Newton,
Harvey, or the pioneers in anthropology and archaeology
would respond. It is far otherwise with Michelangelo,
Rembrandt, Dante, Milton, or Keats. It would be otherwise with Thomas Aquinas, Spinoza, Locke, or Kant. We
might argue all day whether or not the particular artist
or poet or philosopher would feel the present state of art
or poetry or philosophy to be an advance or a retrogres-
sion from the days when he himself was a creative spirit.
There would be no unanimity among us; and more significant still, no agreement between the majority view which
might prevail and that which would have prevailed fifty
years ago.

I recognize how dangerous it is to introduce the concept
of progress as a method of defining an area of intellectual
activity. Therefore, I hasten to say that I am not implying
any hierarchy in my classification. I put no halo over the
words advance or progress; quite the contrary. In terms
of their importance to each of us as human beings, I think
the very subjects which fall outside of my definition of
accumulative knowledge far outrank the others. To am-

plify this point would be to digress too far. I need only ask two questions: How often in our daily lives are we influenced in important decisions by the results of the scientific inquiries of modern times? How often do we act without reflecting the influence of the philosophy and poetry which we have consciously and unconsciously imbibed over many years? A dictator wishing to mold the thoughts and actions of a literate people could afford to leave the scientists and scholars alone, but he must win over to his side or destroy the philosophers, the writers and the artists.

Progress in Theoretical Knowledge and Practice

But to return to the question of accumulative knowledge. If the boundaries of this field of human endeavor are to be measured in terms of progress or the lack of it, must we not include a vast amount of practical as well as theoretical knowledge? Undoubtedly. Indeed, to the nonacademic mind the word progress as applied to man's activities immediately evokes thoughts of synthetic drugs and cars and radios, not Newton's three laws of motion or the quantum theory or Einstein's equation. The distinction between improvement in the practical arts and advances in the sciences would be one of the recurring topics in a course on the Tactics and Strategy of Science. The difference between invention and scientific discovery may in a few instances seem slight but a confusion between the history of the practical arts and the development of science is a fruitful source of misunderstanding about science. Therefore, one of the objectives of even a limited course would be to show by case histories the distinction between advances in mechanical contrivances or primitive chemical processes (such as metallurgy or soap making) and advances in science. In so doing one would try to avoid any false snobbery about the superiority of one activity over the other. Indeed, the interconnections which were frequent even three centuries ago and now form a tight-knit web should be sufficient to emphasize the symbiotic nature of the relation of science to industry.

In the biological sciences it is not industry but commerce and agriculture on the one hand and medicine on the other which are closely related to scientific progress. Again, the connection is a two-way street. The practical arts at first run ahead of the science; only in very recent years have scientific discoveries affected practice to a greater extent than practice has affected science. Returning for a moment to the physical sciences, one may recall that the late Professor L. J. Henderson was fond of remarking that before 1850 the steam engine did more for science than science did for the steam engine. There can be no doubt, of course, that knowledge has been accumulated, classified, and digested to serve practical ends ever since the dawn of civilization. Yet very little is to be learned about the Tactics and Strategy of Science by studying the history of these advances. For they do not form a part of science. Similarly, it may be argued that the progress which has been made in recent centuries in certain nations in the art of government, in the treatment of criminals, in the spread of education, in the mitigation of unequal opportunities and in social reform in general is no part of the social sciences. Such changes bear the same relations to the science of man as do the improvements in manufacturing processes and methods of transportation to the physical sciences (though there seems to be less unanimity today as to the desirability of certain of the social changes).

A Definition of Science

What then is Science? I had originally planned to dodge this question which was first proposed to me as the title of the Terry Lectures by the Yale Committee. I countered with a less ambitious and more ambiguous set of words, namely, "On Understanding Science." But in preparing the manuscript for publication I realize that I have ended by defining science in spite of my resolution to the contrary. Although obviously not competent to follow in the footsteps of the philosophers who have answered the question "What is Science?" as a result of their logical analysis, I have outlined the boundaries of one portion of accumulative knowledge in terms of historical development and called it science. Therefore, I may as well be explicit in regard to my presumption.

As a first approximation, we may say that science emerges from the other progressive activities of man to the extent that new concepts arise from experiments and observations, and the new concepts in turn lead to further experiments and observations. The case histories drawn from the last three hundred years show examples of fruitful and fruitless concepts. The texture of modern science is the result of the interweaving of the fruitful concepts. The test of a new idea is therefore not only its success in correlating the then-known facts but much more its success or failure in stimulating further experimentation or observation which in turn is fruitful. This dynamic quality of science viewed not as a practical undertaking but as development of conceptual schemes seems to me to be close to the heart of the best definition. It is this quality which can be demonstrated only by the historical approach, or else learned by direct professional experience.

To illustrate what I have in mind let us imagine a period in the future when all interest in scientific investigation had ceased but the relatively simple conceptual schemes about matter and energy, the solar system and the basic facts of chemistry of the late nineteenth century were accepted and widely taught. Would the people of that day "understand" science as the late Victorians did? Not to my mind. There would be little difference in their intellectual outlook from that of a people who accept their cosmology as part of a revealed religion. If this be so, the characteristic of the scientific age in which we live lies not in the relative adequacies of our conceptual schemes as to the universe but in the dynamic character of these concepts as interpreted by both professional scientists and laymen. Almost by definition, I would say, science moves ahead.

With all this in mind, I would choose case histories for my projected course from as many areas in the whole field of accumulative knowledge as possible, insisting only that three criteria should be met: (1) The field in question must be one in which there can be no doubt that progress has been substantial in the last century or so (and my test would be the imaginary operation of invoking the judgment of the past.) (2) This progress must be in terms not of practical achievements or mere amassing of data but in terms of changing concepts and evolving conceptual schemes, the result of experiment or observation, yielding in turn new experiments and observations. (3) One or more of the principles common to the Tactics and Strategy of Science must be conveniently illustrated by a study of the case.

These criteria would eliminate from the course consideration of archaeology, philology, and the methods of advancing historical knowledge. But I believe it would be worth a little time nevertheless to point out the great advances in these fields of learning and the limited degree to which the methods used were similar to the methods of science. Progress in mathematics would of course be included in the course to the extent that the students were able to handle the material. Perhaps one may contend that my emphasis on the relation between new concepts and new experiments or new observations would rule out mathematics from the sciences. But since the development of mathematics is also the development of the language of science, I doubt if anyone will be inclined to argue this point against me. At all events, since the emphasis is on the Tactics and Strategy of Science I suggest that the advances in mathematics be illustrated by examples closely connected with physics and astronomy.

In view of the vigor of the current discussion about the nature and scope of the social sciences I should be inclined, if I were in charge of the course, to try to draw at least a few case histories from those disciplines. In so doing consultation with the social scientists would certainly be in order. Psychology would present relatively little difficulty, I imagine, though whether the cases could profitably be drawn from human psychology as well as animal experimentation might be debated. With experiments in vision and audition there should be no trouble but in such important fields of investigation as the learning process and methods of evaluating individual differences in personality, finding cases to illustrate the Tactics and Strategy of Science (according to my standards) might prove very troublesome. And if a hardy instructor in the course in question (assuming it is ever given!) should push farther into sociology, anthropology, and economics, the possible selections would become very few indeed. This statement is in no sense a reflection on the importance of these subjects. For the purpose of expounding the Tactics and Strategy of Science, let me remind you, it is just as important to distinguish between improvements in the practical affairs of life and advances in the science of human behavior (collective and individual) as it is to differentiate the evolution of the practical art of pumping water from the progress of physics. Those who have confidence that we are on the threshold of great advances in the social sciences would probably freely admit that few case histories corresponding to my specifications can now be found outside of the field of psychology. But they would contend that the probability is very high that our grandchildren will be able to study such cases in great number!

With the hopes of the social scientists in mind, may I conclude this chapter by pointing out that our failure to agree on a satisfactory definition of science is in part responsible for some of the confusion in the verbal conflict about the study of man. Quarrels about words are usually without much importance but in this instance there is a significant point at issue. To the extent that the activities of social scientists are really analogous to those of the physical or biological scientist, important lessons may be drawn from past experiences. On the other hand, to the extent that they are analogous to the labors of the archaeologist or philologist, a study of the more spectacular successes in those fields would seem to be in order. And, if, as I suspect, the activities are largely of a practical nature they should be related to the history of the development of the practical arts both before and after the advent of modern science.

Some of the bitterness in the debate comes, to be sure, from the ancient sin of pride; the idea that somehow the scientist is superior to the practical man gets interwoven into the argument. Quite apart from the ordering of the course which I am proposing, I believe it would be of value to differentiate progress in social invention from advances in social science. Further, I suggest that many if not most of the eminent social scientists of our day who are largely concerned with current problems are in fact social *philosophers*. No one should object to the use of this term, for philosophers like mathematicians have always stood at or near the top of the intellectual caste system of our universities. Perhaps if this terminology became current some of the emotional overtones of the word science might be neutralized.

A further discussion of this topic would take me far beyond the province of this book. At the bottom of the controversy about the social sciences and their future, I believe, is a misunderstanding about science even on the part of learned and distinguished men. Therefore, I conclude as might be expected by proclaiming the virtues of my particular pedagogic nostrum. Whether or not an understanding of science can be achieved through the historic route, I trust will become clearer to nonscientific readers who persevere to the end of the present volume.

CHAPTER II

Illustrations from the Seventeenth Century "Touching the Spring of the Air"

IN THIS chapter and the next I shall endeavor by specific examples to illustrate the way in which some knowledge of The Tactics and Strategy of Science might be conveyed. Obviously, I can do no more in a few pages than sketch in the outlines of what might well occupy a class for a month or more. The case histories here presented have no special merit; others would do equally well or better. Indeed, the more usual classic examples I have purposely left aside as being so well known as hardly to warrant another treatment. I refer particularly to Galileo's study of falling bodies and the pendulum, the development of the Copernican theory, and what is sometimes referred to as the Newtonian synthesis. Surely the instructor in any course of the type proposed would want to spend considerable time on the first, and to place the second and third in proper perspective; that is, each case history should be studied only to the extent that it illustrates principles of the Tactics and Strategy of Science.

There is a real danger that in any consideration of historical material one may overemphasize the role of the few brilliant generalizations which from time to time in the last three hundred years have played so important a part in the advancement of science. The contributions we associate with the names of Copernicus, Newton, Joule and Mayer, Carnot, Darwin, Mendel, Planck and Einstein if studied by themselves give quite an erroneous impression of the nature of science. They have been much too prominent in the minds of many who have written about science in general terms. It is therefore to observation and experiment and the less spectacular and less known advances in the sciences that I would primarily direct attention. More can be learned from their study than from the few famous sweeping generalizations which in their time gathered up so much of the past and illumined the future so brightly.

The story I shall relate in this chapter covers a period of less than a hundred years. It centers around the work of Robert Boyle with the air pump and the quantitative investigations that yielded Boyle's Law. But many other individuals including Galileo will also be involved. And I must ask the indulgence of the reader as I skip about in the history of science. The purpose to be served by the study, let me remind you, is not connected with the importance or lack of it of the early studies on air pumps, barometers, and "the spring of the air."

The purpose I should have in mind in leading a class through a group of closely related case histories would be to illustrate the following points which have wide applicability:

1. The influence of new techniques of experimentation and their connection with the practical arts (the development of the air pump is the case at hand).

2. The evolution of new concepts from experiment. (In this chapter we shall witness the replacement of the idea that "nature abhors a vacuum," still serviceable in 1600, by the concept of an atmosphere of a weighable material air, the pressure of this atmosphere varying with the height above the bottom of the "sea of air." We shall also see the beginnings of the fruitful concept of a gas as some-

thing which has a definite "spring" which can be measured quantitatively.)

3. The difficulties of experimentation and the significance of the controlled experiment. (These will be emphasized as well as the need for eternal vigilance in interpreting experiments. While the inherent "cussedness" of inanimate nature is something that only a man who has spent years in experimentation can fully understand, some appreciation of the pitfalls that surround the experimentalist can be acquired by the proper study of the history of science.)

4. The development of science as an organized social activity. (This is well illustrated by any case histories drawn from the seventeenth century; so, too, is the interconnection between science and the general culture of the times. How much of this very interesting material should be introduced into the type of course I propose is an open question. A minimum of it is essential to understanding science, I believe; as a by-product the student will hardly fail to learn something about general cultural history as well.)

The Art of Pumping

Now for the story. Let us start with the state of the art of pumping as it stood at about 1600. There were at hand throughout England and the Continent of Europe a variety of ingenious machines for moving air and water. The bellows made artificial wind for many purposes, particularly for organs, and for quickening the fires used in the metallurgical art. Water was transported out of mines, and for waterworks of towns and villages by force pumps of a simple piston type—huge syringes, so to speak—also by various wheels and screws which do not interest us here, and by lift pumps. The latter are the beginning of

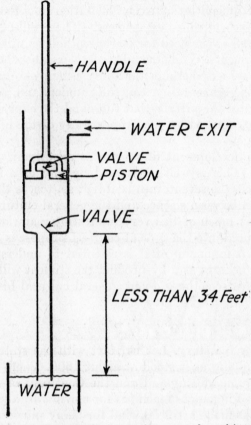

Fig. 1. Diagram of simple lift or suction pump for raising water. The primitive pumps of Galileo's time appear to have had in place of a valve on the piston, a loose packing around the piston which allowed water to pass by on the down stroke but was tight on the up stroke.

our narrative. These pumps, though constructed largely
of wood, were not dissimilar to those once familiar to
everyone on a farm in the United States (see Fig. 1).
They operated by what we now call suction. The explanation of their action in 1600 would have run something as
follows:

The lifting of a close-fitting piston in a tube tends to
create a vacuum; nature abhors a vacuum, as Aristotle
long ago had said; therefore, water rushes up if the tube
in question is properly connected with a cistern, a well,
or a mine shaft full of water. Valves, of a primitive but
effective sort, were so arranged that on a subsequent up
stroke of the piston the water was lifted to the level of
some appropriate exit. Never mind the complications of
valves and mechanical devices nor the movement of water
above the piston; the focal point of our discussion is the
rushing up of the liquid into the abhorred vacuum.

Galileo's Erroneous Conjecture

Galileo related in his *Dialogues Concerning Two New
Sciences*, published in 1638, that a lift pump which failed
to work was once called to his attention. The machine was
in perfect order but it had been asked to do what a workman familiar with pumps said was an impossible task,
namely, draw up water from a cistern for a distance of
more than approximately 34 feet. Probably practical men
long before this day must have recognized that there
were limits to what a suction or lift pump could do. For
example, in one of the illustrations in the famous work
by Agricola on Mining published in 1556 several lift
pumps are shown one above the other; this arrangement
was required because of the limitation which was called to
Galileo's attention. (See Fig. 2)

Now clearly the Aristotelian concept of nature's ab-

From Agricola.

Fig. 2. Reproduction of wood-cut of primitive water pump.

horring a vacuum required amendment as to why this abhorrence only extended to a limited distance. But Galileo, though recognizing that a general principle was involved missed the next step. He believed that water would not rise above 34 feet in a lift pump because the column broke of its own weight. He had the wrong analogy in mind—he was comparing the behavior of a column of water to the breaking point of a copper wire. Here is an example of careful observation, in a sense experimentation (assuming that Galileo tried various pumps at various heights above the water level), and yet a fruitless concept issues even from one of the very great scientists of all times.

Concerning this episode, Martha Ornstein writes, "Galileo was strangely conservative on a few points. For instance, he accepted in Aristotelian fashion the *resistenza del vacuo*, a modified *horror vacui*, as an explanation of why a pump could raise water only thirty-two feet. In the *Discorsi e dimostrazioni matematiche*, Galileo says that, as in the case of a suspended coil of wire there is a length at which its own weight breaks it, so it must be with the column of water raised by the pump. Inasmuch as Galileo knew that air had weight, and had devised a means of weighing it, all this is the more strange, and in a measure enhances the historical interest of the man."

"Strangely conservative on a few points,"—Heaven help us! Does the author of this excellent historical book on scientific societies in the seventeenth century imagine that scientific pioneers first tear up all former conceptual schemes and then try to put something in their place? This passage implies that here was a case of a great man who had a momentary lapse when he failed to introduce a whole new concept into science as a result of pondering on one set of facts. Something easy, but carelessly overlooked!

I call attention to the statement as an illustration of the way a certain degree of misunderstanding about science has been disseminated among laymen by the writing of historians who fail to understand how new concepts only develop after an arduous period of experimentation.

Torricelli's Experiment

Two of Galileo's disciples, Torricelli and Viviani, did find the fruitful trail. But before recounting their story, let us remember that the conceptual scheme implied by the phrase "nature abhors a vacuum" was by no means the nonsense we sometimes imply today. In a limited way this idea explained adequately a number of apparently unrelated phenomena and that is one of the tests of any conceptual scheme. For example, it explained the action of the lift pumps in common use, the adhesion of one piece of wet marble to another, the action of a bellows, one's inability to make a "hole" in a liquid the way one can in a solid, and so on. The fact that water cannot be raised by suction more than thirty-four feet seemed to require an extension of the then current concept, not necessarily a revolutionary new concept. Usually our conceptual schemes grow by an evolutionary process, by the gradual incorporation of a series of amendments, so to speak. In this case a completely new idea came along and rendered obsolete the older one. We shall meet the same phenomenon later in the next chapter when we trace the overthrow of the phlogiston theory.

We can put it down as one of the principles learned from the history of science that a theory is only overthrown by a better theory, never merely by contradictory facts. Attempts are first made to reconcile the contradictory facts to the existing conceptual scheme by some modification of the concept. Only the combination of a new concept with facts contradictory to the old ideas

finally brings about a scientific revolution. And when once
this has taken place, then in a few short years discovery
follows upon discovery and the branch of science in question progresses by leaps and bounds.

With this principle in mind, let us turn back to Italy
in the fifth decade of the seventeenth century. Galileo and
his pupils in Florence are turning over in their minds
various explanations of why nature's abhorrence of a vacuum had a rather sharp and definite limit. At some time
and in some way not recorded, one of them, Torricelli, connected this fact with another fact which was generally accepted even at that time, namely, that air had weight. I
say generally accepted for it was by no means easy to
prove, though Galileo believed he had determined by experiment the approximate ratio of the weights of equal
volumes of air and water. If air had weight, why might
it not exert pressure on the surface of the water in a well
and thus force the water up the lift pump as the piston
rises and produces suction? The height of 34 feet of water
would thus represent the weight of water which this pressure of the air on the surface of the earth could maintain.
Apparently reasoning thus, Torricelli, a young man of 35
in 1643 and Viviani, aged 21, tried some experiments with
another liquid, namely, mercury, which is about 14
times as heavy as water. If the idea they were developing
were correct, the pressure of air which enveloped the earth
would hold up a column of mercury only about 1/14 as
high as that of water, namely, a little more than 2 feet
tall. A column of this height was something that could be
managed with ease. They took a glass tube about a finger's
width in diameter and about 3 feet long, sealed it off at
one end, filled it completely with mercury, and keeping
a finger over the end inverted it in an open vessel of
mercury. (See Fig. 3)

The expected happened, as it sometimes does in this

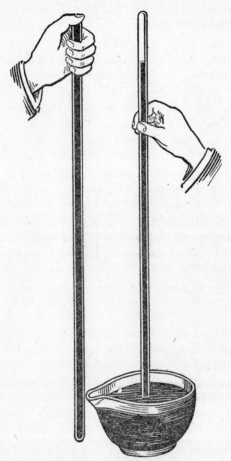

Torricelli's original experiment.

Fig. 3. Balancing the pressure of the air with a mercury column.

type of experimentation when men of ability plan it in advance. The mercury fell to a height of approximately 30 inches above the level of the mercury in the open vessel or trough. The space above in the tube appeared empty. For the first time the world had seen a vacuum, to speak loosely; or, to express the result of the experiment in more accurate terms, a vacuum had been created in the upper end of the tube because the pressure of the atmosphere could support only a column of mercury about 30 inches long. Such a vacuum became known at once as the Torricellian vacuum. Three new techniques had been introduced into science; they are still invaluable. The first was the use of liquid mercury in open vessels and tubes as a medium for experimenting with what we now call gases; the second, closely related, was a method of producing a vacuum; the third was the invention of the barometer, for Torricelli's and Viviani's tube was, of course, a mercury barometer very similar to those still in use today.

Pascal Extends Torricelli's Work

Torricelli's results were made known in 1644 two years after Galileo's death. He survived his brilliant experiments but a few years, dying in 1647. But Viviani lived to continue experimenting with the new devices, the knowledge of which spread rapidly. Pascal, hearing of Torricelli's experiments, repeated them and in 1648 arranged for a mercury barometer to be carried to the top of the Puy-de-Dôme in the central mountain range of France. The trial was made by his brother-in-law, Perier. It showed conclusively that the height of the barometric column diminished progressively as the barometer was set up at higher and higher elevations above the valley. This demonstration was further evidence that the original concept of Torricelli was a fruitful one. But the ideas of the young Florentine were soon to receive support from an entirely different line of experimentation which also seems to have owed its origin to a concern with water pumps of the suction type.

The First Air Pump for Producing Vacua

Water pumps were centuries old but they must have been spreading in the seventeenth century and were certainly being improved. They therefore obtruded themselves on observant and thoughtful men. From such an obtrusion flowed the first erroneous speculation of Galileo which, however, led to two of his pupils taking the right turn. Another gentleman of the seventeenth century also began to inquire into pumps and their action. This was the Burgomaster of Magdeburg, Otto von Guericke, who found that a pump of the lift or suction type he constructed would operate on the third floor of his house, but not on the fourth. Parenthetically, I must note that I resist the temptation to connect this Burgomaster's interest in things mechanical with his service in fortifying various German towns during the Thirty Years' War; his own city was sacked in 1631. Whether the instructor in my hypothetical course would or should resist the temptation is another story, for the digression would enable one to relate the history of science in the first half of the seventeenth century to political and theological upheavals on the Continent.

Sometime between 1635 and 1654 von Guericke's interest in suction pumps for raising water appears to have led him to invent the first air pump by which to produce a vacuum. Whether or not there was any connection between this invention and the work of Galileo's two pupils, Torricelli and Viviani, is one of those intriguing historical questions that can probably never be answered. We can be sure only that by the late 1650's both the Italians and the Burgomaster of Magdeburg were producing vacua though by different methods, and studying what had never been studied before.

Von Guericke's invention in retrospect is a most obvious adaptation of the suction part of a lift water pump. (The

Fig. 4. Von Guericke's Magdeburg hemispheres.

retrospect view of all discoveries and inventions is very misleading and no occasion should be omitted for empha- sizing this fact to the student of the Tactics and Strategy of Science. "Monday morning quarterbacking" will make him familiar with the point at issue.) Von Guericke, in- stead of sucking with a piston and cylinder on a column of water as had been done for centuries by all who used

suction pumps for raising water, tried to suck water out
of a full wooden cask. He used a brass pump. (The improvements implied by this in the art of machine making
would require a word or two in any lengthy treatment of
this subject.) There were several models of this invention
and the usual partial success and failure of the pioneer
attended his efforts. He only attained his results when he
started to pump air as well as water from an enclosed
container, and finally ended by pumping out air alone. He
also found a spherical metal receptacle necessary to stand
the resulting atmospheric pressure. By 1654 he was able
to carry out before the Imperial Diet assembled at Ratis-
bon the famous demonstration of the Magdeburg hemispheres. Two hollow bronze hemispheres were fitted carefully edge to edge and the air contained in the sphere
thus formed removed by a pump. After evacuation the external atmospheric pressure held the two halves together
so firmly that a team of eight horses could not pull them
apart. Once air was admitted through a stopcock, the
hemispheres fell asunder. (See Fig. 4)

Boyle's Improved Air Pump

We now come to the central figure in my story, the
Honorable Robert Boyle, seventh and last son of the great
Earl of Cork. Boyle, who was a proponent of the new experimental philosophy, heard of von Guericke's air pump
through a book published in 1657 by a Jesuit professor
at Würzburg. Boyle proceeded to have an air pump constructed. How much he learned from von Guericke is hard
to say for he writes that such a project had long been on
his mind. His improvements were highly significant for
they included the use of a large glass vessel to be evacuated and *an arrangement for introducing objects into the
vessel.* Thus, experiments could be performed in a vacuum

under continual observation and on a much larger scale than with the Torricellian tube.

Boyle described his pneumatical engine, as he called his pump and his experiments with it in his *New Experiments Physico-Mechanicall Touching the Spring of the Air*, published in 1660. From then on the interest in air pumps spread among the *virtuosi*, as the amateur scientists of the day delighted to call themselves. Huygens a Dutch experimental philosopher saw Boyle's engine in 1661, and returning to the Continent had one made and performed experiments with it. A whole host of experimental observations were let loose on the learned world in the succeeding decades. This is a striking illustration of a principle of wide applicability in the growth of science. A new technique, in this case a new instrument, is suddenly made available and experimentation takes a new turn. The instructor here would obviously point out a few other well-known examples: the telescope exploited by Galileo after being invented in Holland; the microscope and, jumping to our own day, the cyclotron and the betatron.

I need elaborate no further on either this point or the way in which the development of a practical art, namely, pumping water reached a certain point and then influenced scientific development. The development of the art did not represent science, but it influenced the development of science. This aspect of the interconnection of science and society has been a favorite theme for certain writers in the last fifteen years. Again, the instructor might want to digress and trace one or two parallels, and either then or at a later time with other case histories consider the extreme Marxist position as to the influence of economic considerations on the course of scientific history, not failing, however, to show the other side of the medal.

Boyle's new experiments supplemented in an elegant

fashion the work of the Italian and French investigators
on the Torricellian vacuum. For he showed that when a
mercury barometer was so set up that the air above the
lower mercury surface could be withdrawn, the column fell
as would be predicted. On readmitting the air it rose to
the original height.

If we compare the writings of the 1660's with those of
Galileo in 1638 on the same subject, we readily see that
a new concept had evolved as a result of various well-
planned experiments. And this concept had been accepted
by the foremost investigators of the time. Thus the second
point of my opening outline of this chapter, the evolution
of new concept from experiment, is well illustrated by the
history of pneumatics from 1638 to 1660. The new concept was that the earth was surrounded by a "sea of air"
and that since air had weight, the pressure exerted by this
sea was greatest at the bottom, i.e., the surface of the
earth; and as one ascended a mountain, it diminished. The
analogy with water pressure of the ocean was clear and
often made. A vacuum could be created by withdrawing
the air by means of a pump from a closed container or
by taking advantage of the limited height of a column
of liquid (water or mercury) held up by atmospheric
pressure.

The Spring of the Air

Closely associated with the idea of an atmosphere which
exerted a definite pressure which could be measured by
barometers was Boyle's concept of the elasticity of air.
This is so common an idea today that it is hard to imagine
what new facts were required to lead to the development
of so simple a concept. To understand Boyle's mental processes the reader should study the diagram of his air pump
(Figure 5) and read his own account of the operation of

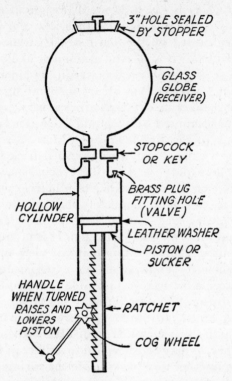

Fig. 5. Simplified diagram of Boyle's air pump.

The following description of the working of the pump is in Boyle's own words: "Upon the drawing down of the sucker (the valve being shut) the cylindrical space, deserted by the sucker, is left devoid of air; and therefore, upon the turning of the key, the air contained in the receiver rusheth into the emptied cylinder. . . . Upon shutting the receiver by turning the key, if you open the valve, and force up the sucker . . . you will drive out almost a whole cylinder full of air; but at the following exsuctions you will draw less and less of air out of the receiver into the cylinder because there will remain less and less air in the receiver itself. . . ."

the engine which is given below. The significant point is that the air in the receiver expands into the vacuum in the cylinder caused by the down stroke of the piston. It does so because air is an elastic medium or as Boyle put it, "there is a spring or elastical power in the air we live in"! No equivalent phenomenon occurs in pumping water.

In modern times we say that air is a very compressible substance as compared with a liquid like water or mercury. "The spring of the air" is an apt phrase, for Boyle felt this spring when his piston was pushed back by the external air toward the end of the evacuation. The same spring is felt on the down stroke of a bicycle pump today when the tire is almost completely inflated.

Thus there evolved another concept from experiment, namely, that air is an elastic medium. It is interesting that Boyle in putting forward this point of view and showing at length how it "explicated" his experiments, did not choose to decide between two possible explanations of why air had a spring. "This notion may perhaps be somewhat further explained," wrote Boyle, "by conceiving the air near the earth to be such a heap of little bodies, lying one upon another, as may be resembled to a fleece of wool. . . . there is yet another way to explicate the spring of the air; namely, by supposing with that most ingenious gentleman, Monsieur *Des Cartes*, that the air is nothing but a congeries or heap of small and (for the most part) of flexible particles, of several sizes, and of all kinds of figures, which are raised by heat (especially that of the sun) into that fluid and subtle ethereal body that surrounds the earth; and by the restless agitation of that celestial matter, wherein those particles swim, are so whirled round, that each corpuscle endeavours to beat off all others from coming within the little sphere requisite to its motion about its own center; . . . according to this doctrine it imports very little, whether the particles of the air have the structure requisite to springs, or be any other form (how irregular soever) since their elastical power is not made to depend upon their shape or structure, but upon the vehement agitation. . . . By these two differing ways, . . . may the springs of the air be explicated. . . . [Yet] am I not willing to declare peremptorily for either of them against the other. . . . I shall decline meddling with a subject, which is more hard to be explicated than necessary to be so by him, whose business it is not, in this letter, to assign the adequate cause of the spring of the air, but only to manifest, that the air hath a spring, and to relate some of its effects."

This quotation when related to the subsequent development of the kinetic theory of gases (which in a qualitative fashion is common knowledge today) might serve as a useful text in the course I am proposing. Boyle clearly distinguishes between his concept of air as an elastic fluid and the *explanation* of this elasticity in terms of pictures or models. This distinction is a useful one in studying the "Tactics and Strategy of Science." The explanations offered for the behavior of gases were at first little more than unbridled speculations, useful as pedagogic devices (as Boyle used the analogy with lamb's wool to show compressibility), but not a necessary part of a conceptual scheme.

The reader may be reminded that the words *theory* and *hypothesis* are frequently employed to describe both conceptual schemes and models, or pictures, "explaining" such schemes. A discussion of the definition of theory and hypothesis is often given in elementary texts, but I think such consideration of doubtful value. Because of the ambiguity it is well, perhaps, to avoid as far as possible both words in discussing the evolution of science.

Boyle when he evinced little interest in alternative explanations which could not be tested by experiment was centuries ahead of his times. Almost all his contemporaries were still largely interested in theories about the universe and cared little or nothing about whether they could be tested by experiment. Only in this century has it become part of the accepted philosophy of science to insist on the necessity of distinguishing an experimentally testable assertion from a proposal to represent the observable facts by certain words or diagrams. This might well be the appropriate point in the course to make reference to the operational point of view clearly stated by Professor Bridgman in his *Logic of Modern Physics*.

Boyle's Controversy with Hobbes and Others

The publication of Boyle's description of his air pump, his experiments and their explanation resulted at once in a controversy. This is, needless to say, a common phenomenon in science. Among his opponents was no less a person than Thomas Hobbes. The difficulties which learned men of the seventeenth century had with new scientific ideas based on experiment can be seen by a study of the controversy. The opponents attacked not only Boyle's statement about the "spring of the air" but even more the idea that a vacuum could exist. Apparently by 1660 learned men were lining up on two opposing sides, the vacuists and the plenists; those who believed in the reality of a vacuum and those who denied it. If the vacua produced by Torricelli and Boyle were *really* vacua (really empty space), how could light and magnetism flow through them? One readily sees how metaphysics and physics got thoroughly entangled in this discussion. Those who denied a vacuum on "general principles" had some ingenious explanation for Boyle's and Torricelli's experiments. One even postulated the existence of an invisible filament, the "funiculus," which kept the mercury in place in a barometer by acting as a sort of thread between the top of the mercury column and the inner surface of the top of the glass tube!

The controversy had one good effect, as almost all controversies do, that of stimulating further experiments. In his second book on the spring and weight of the air (1662), Boyle describes the classic experiments which showed the quantitative relation between volume and pressure of a gas (now called Boyle's Law). Qualitatively what he established was the converse of the effect noted on the Puy-de-Dôme, or in those experiments with his pneumatical engine where the air pressure above the lower mercury of the barometer was diminished. Those experiments showed that *less* than the normal atmospheric pressure would support a *shorter* column of mercury than 30 inches. Boyle now showed that air under *more* than the usual atmospheric pressure would support much *more* than 30 inches of mercury. This he did to confront his opponent who had introduced the *funiculus* to act like a stretched cord upholding the mercury in a Torricellian vacuum. How could any invisible attachment of the mercury column explain these new facts, he asked?

Quantitative Measurements on the Spring of the Air

But for the future, more important than these qualitative observations was the relation he found between the volume of compressed air and the height of the mercury column which put the pressure upon it. To quote his own words, his measurements showed that "common air, when reduced to half its wonted extent, obtained near about twice as forcible a spring as it had before; so this thus comprest air being further thrust into half this narrow room, obtained thereby a spring about as strong again as that it last had, and consequently four times as strong as that of the common air. And there is no cause to doubt, [Boyle continues] that if we had been here furnished with a greater quantity of quicksilver and a very strong tube, we might, by a further compression of the included air, have made it counterbalance the pressure of a far taller and heavier cylinder of mercury. For no man perhaps yet knows, how near to an infinite compression the air may be capable of, if the compressing force be competently increased."

The role of measurement in the evolution of new concepts through experiment would, of course, be a recurring theme in the course which I propose; so, too, would the significance of our increased precision in measurements. The last sentence I have quoted of Boyle points to a much later day when a careful study of the compression of gases showed deviations from Boyle's simple law "that the volume is inversely proportional to the pressure," particularly at high pressure. It foreshadows the study of the liquefaction of gases under high pressure and the discovery of the phenomenon known as the critical state. Depending on what other case histories were to be considered later, the instructor might wish to follow the course of these investigations for two hundred years or more after Boyle. If so, he would point out how new degrees of accuracy in measurement often, but not always, bring to light unsuspected facts.

The Controlled Experiment

Let us now turn to a discussion of the third of the four points I outlined at the beginning of this chapter—the difficulties of experimentation and the significance of the controlled experiment. Illustrations of the inherent diffi-

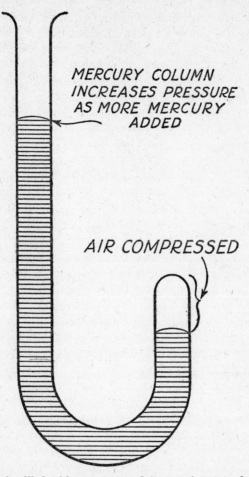

MERCURY COLUMN
INCREASES PRESSURE
AS MORE MERCURY
ADDED

AIR COMPRESSED

Fig. 6. U-tube filled with mercury used in experiment to demonstrate
Boyle's Law.

culty of experimentation are to be found throughout the story I have been recounting. But I shall underline the very great importance of a layman's understanding more about this matter by pointing to two examples, both drawn from Boyle's work. First, the quantitative experiments just mentioned which first demonstrated Boyle's Law. The apparatus Boyle used was very simple—a U-tube of glass of two parallel arms, one short which was sealed off, the other open. By pouring in mercury and tipping the tube it is possible to force mercury into the closed upright a short space while air comes out, and to establish the liquid in the two tubes at the same level. Then the experiment begins. Mercury is poured into the open end and as the pressure increases, the enclosed volume of gas in the short end diminishes (Figure 6). The height of the mercury column in the open end measured vertically upward from the mercury level in the closed end added to the atmospheric pressure determined by a barometer (and measured in "inches of mercury") gives the total pressure; the change in height of the mercury in the closed end measures approximately the change in volume of the enclosed air. Why approximately? Because clearly unless the tube is of absolutely uniform diameter (which is never the case), the change in linear dimension of the column of compressed air is only an approximate measure of the volume.

Boyle's experiment in very nearly its original form is now a common laboratory exercise in elementary physics courses. If fairly uniform tubing can be obtained, the column of mercury need not be more than a few feet to give a fair degree of accuracy. Boyle, on the other hand, did his experimentation in the grand manner. His open tube was so long it had to be in a stair well and he or his assistant went upstairs to pour in the additional increments of mercury. He thus achieved a total pressure of

117 9/16 inches of mercury, 88 7/16 inches more than the barometric pressure of that day which was 29 1/8 inches. Under this pressure the volume of the air in the short tube was compressed from 48 units to 12. (See page 54.) The product of volume and pressure, according to Boyle's Law, is a constant. In the case at hand it will be noted that in point of fact the two numbers are 29 1/8 x 48 or 1,398 initially and 117 9/16 x 12 or 1,411 at the last measurement; the difference is 13 or about 1 part in 140. He thus established the validity of the relation, pressure times volume equals a constant ($PV=$ constant) within this limit of error, but he established it only for common air at room temperature. We now know that some of the variation was experimental error, some inherent in the nature of the gases, for, depending on the gas and the temperature, Boyle's Law holds to a greater or less degree.

There was an important uncontrolled variable in Boyle's experiment which might have introduced very large errors in his measurements. Boyle was aware of the existence of this variable, and did a few rough experiments to show the order of its effect. I refer, of course, to the influence of temperature. All the new experimental philosophers of Boyle's time knew that the application of heat had an expansive effect on air; indeed, that is the way Galileo long ago had sought to weigh air. He had weighed a vessel, then heated it, thus driving some of the air out, sealed it off, and weighed it again. Furthermore, rough estimates of temperature at this period were made with a thermoscope whose action depended on the change of volume of air with change in temperature.

Boyle cooled his compressed air with a wet cloth and warmed it with a candle flame and noticed a slight change. He drew no conclusions from these changes except to say that he had no doubt that "the expansion of the air would,

A TABLE OF THE CONDENSATION OF THE AIR (Boyle's original data)

A	B	C	D	E
48	00		29 2/16	29 2/16
46	01 7/16		30 9/16	30 6/16
44	02 13/16		31 15/16	31 12/16
42	04 6/16		33 8/16	33 3/7
40	06 3/16		35 5/16	35
38	07 14/16		37	36 15/19
36	10 2/16		39 5/16	38 7/8
34	12 8/16		41 10/16	41 2/17
32	15 1/16		44 3/16	43 11/16
30	17 15/16		47 1/16	46 3/5
28	21 3/16		50 5/16	50
26	25 3/16	Added to 29 2/8 makes	54 5/16	53 10/13
24	29 11/16		58 13/16	58 5/8
23	32 3/16		61 5/16	60 18/23
22	34 15/16		64 6/16	63 5/11
21	37 15/16		67 7/16	66 4/7
20	41 9/16		70 11/16	70
19	45		74 2/16	73 11/19
18	48 12/16		77 14/16	77 2/3
17	53 11/16		82 12/16	82 4/7
16	58 2/16		87 14/16	87 7/8
15	63 15/16		93 1/16	93 3/5
14	71 1/16		100 7/16	99 6/7
13	78 11/16		107 13/16	107 7/13
12	88 7/16		117 9/16	116 4/8

A. The number of equal spaces in the shorter leg, that contained the same parcel of air diversely extended.

B. The height of the mercurial cylinder in the longer leg, that compressed the air into those dimensions.

C. The height of the mercurial cylinder, that counterbalanced the pressure of the atmosphere.

D. The aggregate of the two last columns, B and C, exhibiting the pressure sustained by the included air.

E. What that pressure should be according to the hypothesis, that supposes the pressures and expansions to be in reciprocal proportion.

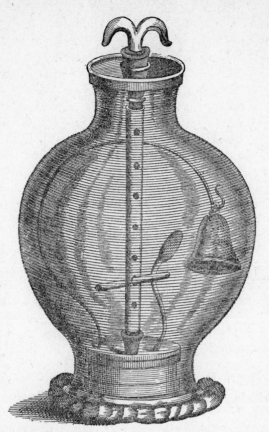

Fig. 7. Boyle's Contrivance for Ringing a Bell in a Vacuum. The turning of the "key" at the top rotates the vertical cylinder carrying the crossbar and thus causes the hammer on the end of the spring to strike the bell. The evacuated glass container has a wide opening at the bottom through which various contrivances can be introduced. It is sealed to a flat iron plate by a ring of cement as shown. The air is removed through a pipe connected with a hole in the plate under the center of the receiver. This type of receiver was part of Boyle's second and advanced model of a pneumatical engine. The improvements allowed many new experiments *in vacuo* to be performed; this illustrates again the significance of improved techniques.

notwithstanding the weight that opprest it, have been made conspicuous, if the fear of unseasonably breaking the glass had not kept us from increasing the heat." Yet I feel sure that to so sure-footed an experimenter as Boyle, this experiment laid to rest any doubts which might have been in his mind that changes of temperature of the room during the experiment would have affected the result. It was more than a hundred years later (1787) that the exact relationship between temperature and volume of gases was worked out by Charles. Indeed, in Boyle's day the very concept of temperature was of a most qualitative sort. A gas expands about 1/300th of its volume for every degree rise in temperature (Centigrade). Let it be noted that if the world had been so constructed that the value was 1/10th instead of 1/300th, the lack of control of temperature would have played havoc with the early measurements. However, if that had been the case, Boyle's qualitative observation would have alerted him to the danger.

This point would deserve considerable elaboration by the instructor as all who have spent their lives making measurements will heartily agree.

The essence of the controlled experiment is, of course, the control of the relevant variables such as temperature, pressure, light, and presence of other materials, particularly small amounts of air and water. This is always a question of degree, and ways of estimating the effect of lack of control are of first importance. Progress in a given area often depends on recognizing what are in fact the relevant variables and devising methods of measuring and controlling them. Errors frequently spring from the overlooking of important variable factors. A study of Boyle's experiments with water in his evacuated receiver might be used to good advantage in this connection. He was interested in determining the expansion of water when the atmospheric pressure was removed. But he failed to appreciate fully the difficulties due to dissolved air in the water and did not realize that water will boil at room temperature if the pressure above the liquid is sufficiently reduced. New concepts like "dissolved air," "vapor pressure," "boiling point as a function of pressure" were required before the variables could be controlled. The interplay between advances in experimentation and the development of new concepts is once again evident from these examples.

Difficulties of Experimentation

In addition to directing attention to the difficulties which beset all those who make quantitative measurements, I suggest that the early history of pneumatics could be used in another way. A whole series of experiments could be studied which dealt with the question whether or not sound was conducted in a vacuum. The controversy never rose to a major level, as everyone seemed to agree that probably air was the medium through which sound was transmitted. For those interested in the tactics of science, however, this work is of interest as showing the great difficulties of settling a question by experiment. It would appear easy to set a bell up in a glass container, evacuate the air, then set the bell ringing and notice whether or not it could be heard. The difficulties were these: (1) how to ring a bell by distant control before the days of electricity; (2) the vacua available by either the Torricellian method or the air pump were far from perfect; (3) the bell must be somehow supported and, as we now know, solid media conduct sound.

Ingenious methods were used to circumvent these difficulties, but to silence the bell proved very hard. Boyle's experiments as always are worth studying. He hung a watch in a receiver by a thread and had the satisfaction of hearing no sound of its ticking when the receiver was evacuated; on the admission of a little air the sound was heard. But with a bell on solid support he found little change on exhausting the air in his first trials. Later he contrived to mount a bell in such a fashion that the sound could not easily travel along the support. He also hung a watch "with a good alarm" by a thread "because it might be suspected that if the watch were suspended by its own silver chain the tremulous motion of its sounding bell might be propagated by the chain to the upper part of the glass. . . ." In both cases no sound was heard after the exhaustion of the air from the vessel.

These studies of bells in vacua may seem too trivial to warrant attention. But I believe that the proper study of such simple cases, full of pitfalls, will leave in the student's mind a clearer understanding of experimental science than can often be obtained in an introductory course in physics or chemistry. There are better examples undoubtedly. I have mentioned this one in particular because it is part of the general account of the seventeenth-century study of air. In the same category are the attempts to weigh the air. The history of the gradual approach to something like an accurate estimate of its weight is another case history worthy of attention. Only by understanding the difficulties encountered in trying to do what now seems simple can a student appreciate the hurdles which must be surmounted in modern experiments of which we, for the most part, hear only the conclusions.

A Recapitulation

Let me now recapitulate briefly the three points which I hope a study of the spring of the air would illustrate.

First, the importance of new techniques as illustrated by
the use of mercury to create a Torricellian vacuum (and
a barometer) and the invention of the air pump; as a subtopic, the influence of a well-developed practical art like
pumping on scientific progress is twice emphasized (by
reference to Galileo's unfruitful speculation and von
Guericke's highly profitable invention of the air pump).
Second, the evolution of new concepts from experiments
has been shown in two instances—the replacement of the
Aristotelian *horror vacui* by the idea of an atmosphere
exerting pressure, and the concept of air as an elastic
fluid. As subtopics we note that new facts may modify a
conceptual scheme or when combined with a new concept
may overthrow an older idea; we also note in Boyle's work
on the spring of the air the difference between a conceptual scheme closely tied to experiment and explanations of
the scheme which are not at the time susceptible to experimental test. (Because the words theory and hypothesis are
often applied to both a conceptual scheme and the explanation of the scheme in terms of a mechanical analogy
or model, the words have perhaps come to have both too
limited and too wide an application). Third, the case
histories in question illustrate almost continually the difficulties of experimentation, and the study of the transmission of sound in air and in a vacuum is especially recommended as of considerable pedagogic value. In particular,
attention has been called to the importance of the controlled experiment. This is illustrated by a consideration
of the effect of temperature on the quantitative measurements which first showed the relations between the volume
and pressure of a gas. Another subtopic, namely, the requisite accuracy required to establish a new relationship
can be introduced by a discussion of the sources of error
in Boyle's experiment.

Science as an Organized Social Activity

The fourth and last of the points outlined initially was the development of science as an organized social activity. This can be illustrated excellently by the case histories considered in this chapter. Indeed, any case histories drawn from the second half of the seventeenth century are ideal for this purpose. For this was the century in which the famous scientific societies were founded and during which they played perhaps their most significant role. For those who would understand science both the modern methods of publishing scientific results and the way these methods originated are of great importance. Case histories from the seventeenth century will illustrate the latter; in connection with this study a brief glimpse of the vast literature of science that exists in the twentieth century would be in order. The layman should know something of the methods of indexing and compiling this literature and gain some understanding of how, in spite of the volume of material, scientific news now travels faster than ever before. Some ardent advocates of a greater degree of national planning talk as though priceless gems of science were every day being hidden under a mound of unread papers; they imply that discoveries are not being followed up as they should be, that fruitful fields are left unexplored. One of the objects of understanding science should be to correct this almost totally false picture of the current scene.

Science and Society in the Seventeenth Century

A consideration of Robert Boyle's life is almost ideal for one who wishes to discuss science and society in the seventeenth century. Economics, politics, religion, scientific societies, universities, all these topics can be treated in as much length as desired once the subject of "Robert Boyle, his life and times" has been introduced. Boyle was the son of the Great Earl of Cork, a self-made Englishman of the tough Elizabethan period of exploration and exploitation. Many of his close relatives were prominent actors in the great drama of the Civil Wars, wars which opened by the Irish uprising of 1640 which devastated his father's vast estates. Too young to take an active part in the war between King and Parliament, Boyle can, nevertheless, be classed as being on the moderate Puritan side. His residence in Oxford, 1649–58, coincided with the ascendancy of this same Puritan element in that University, then purged of Royalists and Anglicans by a Parliamentary Commission. Though holding no official position in the University, he was a close associate of many in that famous group of young men led by the Warden of Wadham College, John Wilkins, Cromwell's brother-in-law. From the gathering of these amateur scientists and philosophers came the Royal Society, founded just after the Restoration. How these men happened to be in Oxford rather than Cambridge, what they did to reform the University on the one hand and protect the colleges from the extreme Puritans on the other, is full of interest. Portions of the story might well be introduced to illustrate the interrelations between social, religious, and political forces in the early days of science.

Such an excursion into the history of England of the Cromwellian and early Restoration period would also enable the instructor to call attention to the complex interplay of those cultural influences which determine the climate of opinion. It is at this point, for example, that some discussion of Bacon's and Descartes' philosophy should be introduced. The writings of a number of historians in the last twenty-five years have stressed the fact

that of the first members of the Royal Society a considerable majority were Puritan sympathizers or had Puritan
connections. A consideration of the possible significance of
this fact leads one to further speculation along the lines
made famous by Max Weber and others connecting the
Protestant ethic, the rise of capitalism, and the phenomenal growth of scientific activity in the seventeenth century.

Then, lest one become too engrossed with one country
and the cultural effects of the Reformation, a jump to
Catholic Florence would be in order. There, at the same
identical period, we find another group of young men
earnestly at work on experiments. Under the personal
leadership of two Medici brothers, Ferdinand II and
Leopold, some of Galileo's students, including Viviani
(Torricelli's co-worker) were banded together for experimental work from 1651–57. Then for ten years, 1657–67,
they became the famed Accademia del Cimento which
much more than the British Royal Society was a genuine
coöperative experimental effort. The members worked together and published together, carrying forward many of
the ideas implicit in Galileo's later work and that of Torricelli. Then their patron Leopold Medici became a cardinal and the academy dissolved. An interesting comparison
between the histories of the two contemporary groups,
English and Italian, can be made, not without profit to a
student's general understanding of the crosscurrents of
modern history.

But the danger in the type of course I am suggesting
will not be the danger of neglecting to put the case histories in their proper historical setting, but rather that
the examination of the setting may take too much time.
After all, I am suggesting a course in the Tactics and
Strategy of Science, not one on European cultural history

as illustrated by episodes in science, though the latter might be of value in the education of future scientists and engineers. Therefore, the role of the scientific societies in forwarding the new philosophy and sponsoring the publication of books and journals such as the *Philosophical Transactions* (begun in 1665) would be the matter of prime attention. The contrast between what was done through these organized social activities and what could not be done through the universities is striking. Here again Boyle's residence in Oxford at the one fleeting moment when perhaps the two "fountains of learning" of England might have been set flowing in new channels makes an appropriate introduction to an important story. Also, the contrast between England and Italy must be made. Looking back beyond the period of the case history at hand, we find in the sixteenth century and the first half of the seventeenth century the early dawn of experimental and observational science in the Italian universities. Of this dawn neither Oxford nor Cambridge, in the throes of religious controversy at the same period, showed the slightest sign. Later there was a brief period of excitement at Oxford in regard to the new experimental philosophy. Yet in the seventeenth and eighteenth centuries the universities of neither country became the home of science.

Such facts make all the more important a study of the scientific societies and the role of the amateurs by whose labors alone science advanced for more than two hundred years. How these amateurs earned their living or inherited the where-with-all to live is part of the same story. In the seventeenth century in England the hereditary wealth of a new aristocracy or the not-too-onerous positions in the established church or a few educational posts supported the *virtuosi;* in France the members of the new scientific academy received pensions from the King. A hundred years later in the two countries we shall see a chemical revolution brought about during the spare hours of a dissenting clergyman and an official of the expiring Bourbon government. By reference to such facts, there can be left in the student's mind no doubt that science is indeed a social process. He will also be reminded that western society in the development of its modern culture has at times worked in mysterious ways its wonders to perform.

In these days when every citizen is expected to have opinions on the relation between government, education, and scientific research and development, surely some appreciation of the past complexities of the relation of science to society should be part of a general education. And from what period of history can one learn more than from the century of genius—the seventeenth—which was in many ways the cradle of our present era. With such thoughts in mind, a considerable portion of the case histories in the course I am proposing might well be from this period. In the next chapter, I shall consider a much more sophisticated era—the late eighteenth century. A discussion of some early experiments in electricity and in chemistry will illustrate certain other principles which seem of importance to the Tactics and Strategy of Science.

CHAPTER III

Illustrations from the Eighteenth Century Concerning Electricity and Combustion

AS THOSE who have read the first two chapters are well aware, this book is in no sense a presentation of the history of science or of any branch of science. The objective is to indicate how certain principles might be taught by illustrations drawn from the development of science. In the last chapter a study of the seventeenth-century experiments with barometers, air pumps, and vacua illustrated certain principles. These were four in number: (1) the influence of new techniques; (2) the evolution of new concepts from experiment; (3) the difficulties of experimentation and the significance of the controlled experiment; (4) the development of science as an organized social activity.

In this chapter two case histories are presented both drawn from the end of the eighteenth century. The first concerns the discovery of the electric battery, the second concerns the chemical revolution which placed our knowledge of combustion on a sound basis. Both can be used to illustrate the four points just named, but each is particularly suitable for emphasizing certain other important principles which I shall introduce for the first time in connection with the discussion of the new material.

The Role of the Accidental Discovery

The layman is frequently confused in regard to the role of the accidental discovery on the one hand and the planned experiment on the other. This is particularly true in connection with the development of new techniques and the evolution of new concepts from experiment. The case history which I recommend for a study of these topics is the work of Galvani and Volta on the electric current. This case history illustrates the fact that an accidental discovery may lead by a series of experiments (which must be well planned) to a new technique or a new concept or both; it also shows that in the exploration of a new phenomenon the experiments may be well planned without any "working hypothesis" as to the nature of the phenomenon, but that shortly an explanation is sure to arise. A new conceptual scheme will be evolved. This may be on a grand scale and have wide applicability, or may be strictly limited to the phenomenon in question. A test of the new concept or group of concepts in either instance will probably lead to new discoveries and the eventual establishment, modification, or overthrow of the conceptual scheme in question.

Galvani's Discoveries

The case history begins with certain observations made by Luigi Galvani, an Italian physician, a professor at Bologna, some time before 1786. This investigator noted the twitching of a frog's leg when the crural nerves were touched by a metallic scalpel in the neighborhood of an electrostatic machine from which sparks were drawn. *He followed up his observation.* At this point in a course on the Tactics and Strategy of Science the instructor would wax eloquent. He would remind the class that time and time again throughout the history of science the consequences of following up or not following up accidental discoveries have been very great. The analogy of a general's taking advantage of an enemy's error or a lucky break, like the capture of the Remagen bridge, could hardly fail to enter the discussion. Pasteur once wrote that "chance favors only the prepared mind." This is excellently illustrated by the case history at hand. The Dutch naturalist, Swammerdam, had previously discovered that if you lay bare the muscle of a frog in much the same way as Galvani did, grasp a tendon in one hand and touch the frog's nerve with a scalpel held in the other hand, a twitching will result. But Swammerdam never followed up his work. Galvani did. In his own words, "I had dissected and prepared a frog . . . and while I was attending to something else, I laid it on a table on which stood an electrical machine at some distance. . . . Now when one of the persons who were present touched accidentally and lightly the inner crural nerves of the frog with the point of a scalpel all the muscles of the legs seemed to contract again and again. . . . Another one who was there, who was helping us in electrical researches, thought that he had noticed that the action was excited when a spark was discharged from the conductor of the machine. Being astonished by this new phenomenon he called my attention to it, who at that time had something else in mind and was deep in thought. Whereupon I was inflamed with an incredible zeal and eagerness to test the same and to bring to light what was concealed in it." *

Galvani did not succeed in bringing to light all that was concealed in the new phenomenon. But he proceeded far enough to make the subsequent discoveries inevitable. In a series of well-planned experiments he explored the obvious variables, but without a clear-cut, over-all hypothesis. This is the usual situation when a new phenomenon is encountered by a gifted experimenter. A series of work-

* Reprinted by permission from *A Source Book in Physics* by W. F. Magie, copyrighted, 1935, by the McGraw-Hill Book Company, Inc.

ing hypotheses spring to mind, are tested and either discarded or incorporated into a conceptual scheme which gradually develops. For example, Galvani first determined whether or not sparks had to be drawn from the electrical machine in order to occasion twitching. He found "Without fail there occurred lively contractions . . . at the same instant as that in which the spark jumped. . . ."

The nerves and muscles of the frog's leg constituted a sensitive detector of an electric charge. Galvani found that not only must a spark be passing from the electrostatic machine but the metallic blade of the scalpel must be in contact with the hand of the experimenter. In this way a small charge originating from the electrical disturbance, namely the spark, passed down the conducting human body through the scalpel to the nerve. So far the physician was on sound and fruitful ground. There now occurred one of those coincidences which more than once has initially baffled an investigator but eventually led to great advances. The frog's leg could under certain circumstances act not only as a sensitive electrical detector but as a source of electricity as well. When this happened, the electricity self-generated so to speak actuated the detector. One can readily see that the superposition of these two effects could be most bewildering and misleading. This was particularly so since the conditions under which the frog's leg became a source of electricity were totally unconnected with any electrical phenomena then known. The variable was the nature of the metal or I should say metals used. For Galvani discovered and duly recorded that the electrostatic machine could be dispensed with if the leg and the nerve were connected together by two *different* metals. Under these conditions the twitching occurred. (The experiment was usually performed as follows: a curved rod was made to touch simultaneously both a hook passing through the spinal cord of the frog and the "muscles of the leg or the feet.") "Thus, for example," wrote Galvani, "if the whole rod was iron or the hook was iron . . . the contractions either did not occur or were very small. But if one of them was iron and the other brass, or better if it was silver (silver seems to us the best of all the metals for conducting animal electricity) there occur repeated and much greater and more prolonged contractions."

Galvani had discovered the principle of the electric battery without knowing it. His two metals separated by the moist animal tissue were a battery, the frog's leg the detector. Every reader can perform the equivalent of Galvani's experiment himself. A copper coin and a silver one placed above and below the tongue when touched together produce in the tongue a peculiar "taste." A very small electric current flows and our tongue records the fact through a series of interactions of electricity and nerves much in the same way as did Galvani's "prepared" frogs. Not having a suspicion of all this, however, Galvani developed a conceptual scheme (an hypothesis on the grand scale, we might say) to account for all the phenomena in terms of what was then known about electricity which was derived entirely from experiment with electrostatic machines. Having found outside electrical disturbances unnecessary (when he unwittingly used the *right* metallic combination!) the experiments, he says, "cause us to think that possibly the electricity was present in the animal itself." Galvani's following up of an accidental discovery by a series of controlled experiments had led to a recording of the significant facts, but it was to be another Italian who developed the fruitful concept. It was Volta who in the late 1790's, continuing the study of the production of electricity by the contact of two different metals, invented the electric battery as a source of what we now often call Galvanic electricity.

Volta's Invention of the Electric Battery

Alessandro Volta (1745–1827) of Padua had earlier invented a new form of instrument for detecting small charges of electricity. He began by agreeing with Galvani about animal electricity and went about studying it. With his new instrument, a sensitive condensing electrometer, Volta explored various combinations of variables related to Galvani's early experiments and found that the frog could be eliminated in favor of almost any moist material. This discovery might be considered an example of the accidental discovery, but if so it is of a different order from that of Galvani. Explorations with new techniques and tools, if undertaken in a more or less orderly fashion, almost always turn up unexpected facts. In this sense a great majority of new facts of science are accidental discoveries. But the difference between this sort of experience and the example afforded by Galvani's work is obvious. Volta's new discovery amounted, of course, to the invention of the electric battery; for he showed that electricity was produced when two different metals were separated by water containing salt or lye. This was most conveniently done by using moistened paper. In a letter to the President of the Royal Society of London in 1800 Volta wrote "30, 40, 60 or more pieces of copper, or rather of silver, each in contact with a piece of tin, or of zinc, which is much better, and as many layers of water or of some other liquid which is a better conductor than pure water, such as salt-water or lye and so forth, or pieces of pasteboard or of leather, etc. well soaked with these liquids; . . . such an alternative series of these three sorts of con-

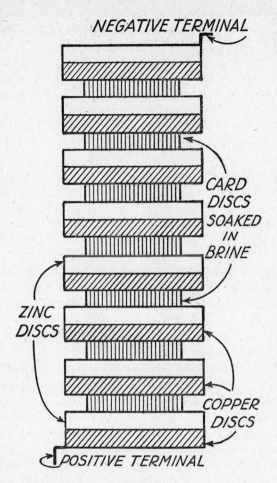

Fig. 8. One form of Volta's battery or pile.

ductors always in the same order, constitutes my new instrument; which imitates . . . the effects of Leyden jars.
. . ." (see Figure 8). This new battery was a source of electricity different from the electrostatic generator already known in 1800; it was the first source of continuous current. The battery produced electricity of low potential but of considerable quantity (low voltage, relatively high amperage); the sparks from a frictional machine are brief spasms of current of high potential but very low amperage.

There was a hot controversy between Galvani's disciples (Galvani died in 1798) and Volta about whether or not there was such a thing as animal electricity, and what caused the twitching of the frog's leg in the first experiments. Volta soon lost interest in the quarrel and devoted his attention to the study of his new battery. Today we have a rather complete and highly satisfactory conceptual scheme in which all the facts about electric batteries find their place. This is not the case, however, with observations about muscles, nerves, and electric currents in animal tissue. In this field one working hypothesis still replaces another and new experiments are still throwing new light on an ancient phenomenon. In a sense, we have not yet finished with Galvani's very first observation, but have finished with Volta's discovery. The original controversy centered on the question, is there animal electricity? This has now become largely a meaningless question, but in attempting to find an answer Volta discovered the electric battery. Such is often the course of scientific history. We end by solving a problem other than the one first at issue.

Another case history which illustrates the role of the accidental discovery, the well-planned experiments by which it may be followed up, the role of the working hypothesis, the development of an hypothesis on the grand scale, and the rapid emergence of both a new technique and a new concept is furnished by a study of the discovery of X rays. The story is familiar to all scientists though perhaps it is not generally known that before Roentgen announced his discovery, several other investigators had noticed the fogging of photographic plates near an electric discharge tube. Roentgen followed up his accidental observation. For pedagogic purposes in a course on the Tactics and Strategy of Science this case history could be used to supplement the one just given or in place of it. Roentgen's work is both simpler and more complex than Galvani's and Volta's; the experimentation and reasoning are more straightforward, but to understand the discovery of the X rays the student should have a considerable background of physics. Therefore, the eighteenth-century example is better in that it almost explains itself as far as technical terms are involved. On the other hand, it is more remote and perhaps less interesting to the average layman.

The Revolutionary Effect of New Techniques

Both the case of the discovery of the electric battery and that of X rays show in a dramatic fashion a point I referred to in the last chapter, namely, that a new technique may have an almost revolutionary effect. With the new electric battery in the beginning of the nineteenth century, Humphry Davy and many others discovered all sorts of new electrochemical and physical phenomena; from them in turn came in rapid succession new techniques and new concepts. Likewise in our own day after the publication of an account of the X-ray tube, new experimental facts came forth in torrents. Tremendous spurts in the progress of the various sciences are almost always connected with the development of a new technique or the sudden emergence of a new concept. It is as though a group of prospectors were hunting in barren ground and suddenly struck a rich vein of ore. All at once everyone works feverishly and the gold begins to flow.

Two Further Principles in the Tactics and Strategy of Science

Let us now turn to the second case history to be considered in this chapter. It is an example drawn from the history of chemistry in the second half of the eighteenth century, and, it is only fair to warn the reader, a most complicated case. Perhaps too much effort is required to master the facts involved to make this a good example for the layman. But I believe it should be included in the course I am proposing because in it two important principles in the Tactics and Strategy of Science are illustrated in a peculiarly striking fashion. These principles are as follows:

First, a useful concept may be a barrier to the acceptance of a better one if long-intrenched in the minds of scientists.

Second, experimental discoveries must fit the time; facts may be at hand for years without their significance being realized; the total scientific situation must be favorable for the acceptance of new views.

The Overthrow of the Phlogiston Theory

The case history which illustrates excellently these two important points might be entitled "the overthrow of the phlogiston theory" or "Lavoisier's work on combustion in the 1770's." As indicated by the first phrase the case also affords a classic example of the mustering of evidence pro and con when two rival concepts are in collision. This phenomenon though frequent is usually so transient in the history of science as to be hard to capture for purposes of historical study. In the investigation of combustion the normal progress of science was, so to speak, delayed; this fact, in a sense, accounts for why a study of this difficult passage in scientific history is of special significance to those interested in the Tactics and Strategy of Science.

The easiest way to understand the revolution in chemistry associated with the name of Lavoisier is first to describe the phenomena in question in terms of modern concepts; then to show how for nearly a hundred years everyone was thoroughly confused. This pedagogic device would have to be used by the instructor in the course I am suggesting. It involves the dogmatic statement of a certain amount of popularized physics and chemistry, but I doubt if the presentation would be much more arbitrary in this respect than most freshman courses. Indeed, some of the material might be said to be common knowledge today.

Almost every high-school graduate "knows" (I put quotation marks around the word) that air is primarily a mixture of oxygen gas and nitrogen gas; furthermore, when a candle or a match or a cigarette "burns," heat and light are being evolved by a chemical reaction involving oxygen. This is called "combustion." If we burn enough material in a closed space, the combustion stops because the oxygen is used up. What burns? Some but not all of the students will say that in the cases mentioned it is a group of carbon compounds, and some will add that the products of combustion are carbon dioxide, CO_2 and water, H_2O. Anyone who has an elementary knowledge of chemical symbols usually loves to share the information! Suppose you heat molten tin in air at a high temperature for a long time, and the bright metal becomes covered with a scum, obviously not a metal. What has happened? A combination with oxygen—an oxide is formed—the bright boys and girls answer. Correct. Suppose we heat this non-metallic substance, an oxide, with carbon. What would happen? The carbon would combine with the oxygen, giving an oxide of carbon and leaving the metal. This is what happens in making iron from iron ore, the very bright boy tells you.

All very simple and plain. And you can set students to work in high-school laboratories to prove it. Yet it is an historic fact that at the time of the American Revolution not one philosopher or experimentalist out of one hundred could have given you an inkling of this explanation which we now designate as "correct." Instead, they would have talked learnedly of "phlogiston," a name probably totally unfamiliar to all but the chemists who read this book. Nearly a hundred years after Newton, and still everyone was thoroughly bewildered by such a simple matter as combustion! This fact needs to be brought home to all who would understand science and who talk of the "scientific method."

The chemical revolution was practically contemporary with the American Revolution and, of course, just preceded the French Revolution. Lavoisier, the man who singlehanded but building on the work of others made the revolution, lost his head at the hands of the Revolutionary Tribune in 1794 (though he was by no means hostile to the basic aims of the great social and political upheaval). Whether or not he was betrayed by a scientific colleague (Fourcroy) who at least was an ardent supporter of the extreme party then in power, is an intriguing historical question.; its study would be a by-product of this case history in which certain students would take great interest. Likewise, the fact that another prominent figure in the final controversy was Priestley, a Unitarian clergyman, who was made an honorary citizen by the French Assembly and then fled to America in the very year of Lavoisier's execution to escape a reactionary English mob, adds zest to the story. There is no lack of material to connect science with society in the late eighteenth century, though the connection I think is more dramatic than significant; at all events, for keeping up students' interest it can hardly be surpassed.

The Classic Experiment on the Role of Oxygen in Combustion

The chemical revolution took place during the years 1772–78. By the later date Lavoisier had made clear to the scientific world the role of oxygen in combustion. His classic experiment, often described in elementary textbooks, was as follows: Mercury heated in common air produces a red material (an oxide we would say, a "calx" to the chemists of the eighteenth century). In a closed space about one fifth of the air disappears. The red material weighs more than the metal from which it was formed. Therefore, something has disappeared from the air and combined with the metal. The red material, the oxide or calx, is next strongly heated in an enclosed space with the sun's rays brought to a focus by a large lens or "burning glass," a gas is evolved and the metal regenerated. The new gas is the "something" which disappeared from the original air, for the amount is the same, and the calx has lost weight in the right amount. The new gas (oxygen) mixed with the residue from the first experiment yields a mixture which is identical with common air. (Figures 9 and 10.)

The experiments are simple, the proof appears to be complete. (Lavoisier, of course, generalized far beyond the case of mercury.) But the new conceptual scheme was

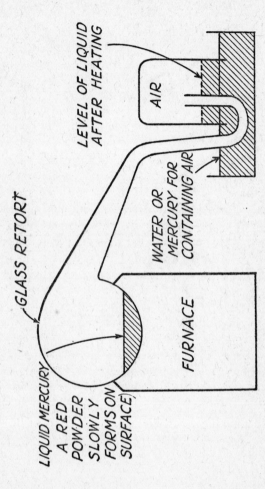

GLASS RETORT

LIQUID MERCURY
A RED
POWDER
SLOWLY
FORMS ON
SURFACE)

LEVEL OF LIQUID
AFTER HEATING

AIR

WATER OR
MERCURY FOR
CONTAINING AIR

FURNACE

Fig. 9. Mercury heated in air absorbs oxygen.

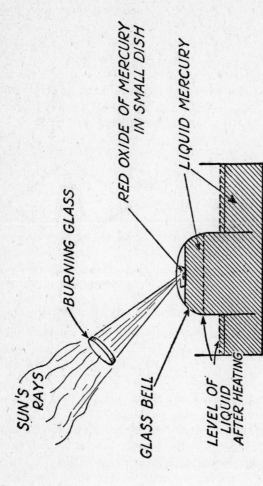

SUN'S RAYS

BURNING GLASS

RED OXIDE OF MERCURY IN SMALL DISH

LIQUID MERCURY

GLASS BELL

LEVEL OF LIQUID AFTER HEATING

Fig. 10. Red oxide of mercury heated very hot evolves oxygen.

(The temperature in this experiment must be very much higher than in the formation of the oxide.)

by no means accepted at once with great acclaim. Quite the contrary. Lavoisier had to drive home his points with telling arguments. Slowly his French contemporaries were won over, but Priestley and Watt of the steam-engine fame and Cavendish and scores of others continued to cling to the phlogiston theory for a decade. Priestley's case is particularly interesting. This English experimenter had actually provided Lavoisier with an important clue when in 1774 he told him about his preparation of oxygen gas by heating red oxide of mercury. But Priestley died in 1804 without ever being converted to the new doctrine.

Why was there this reluctance to modify ideas in the light of beautifully clear experiments, and why were the men of the eighteenth century so long in getting on the right track? There were two reasons: first, one conceptual scheme—the phlogiston theory—had acquired an almost paralyzing hold on their minds; and second, elucidating the facts necessary to overthrow the theory involved experiments with gases which were then extremely difficult.

The Significance of the Phlogiston Theory

The phlogiston theory in its day was, we must first realize, a long step forward. In the sixteenth and seventeenth centuries those who were interested in making some sense out of what we now call chemistry were wandering in a bewildering forest. From the alchemists and the practical men, particularly the metal makers, they had acquired a mass of apparently unrelated facts and strange ideas about "elements." The earth, air, fire, and water concept of Aristotle was still hovering over them. Boyle in his *Skeptical Chymist* did a little, but not much, to clear a space in the tangled underbrush of fact and fancy so closely interwoven and cemented by strange words. Let us look at some of the common phenomena that had to be explained by Newton and his contemporaries, that is to say, fitted into a conceptual scheme. Metals could be obtained by heating certain materials with charcoal (the ancient art of winning metals from their ores). Metals were at first sight very much the same; they had similar superficial properties. Even today the classification of metal and nonmetal appeals at once to a layman. Other solids were called "earths" (oxides for us today) or else, like charcoal or sulfur, they were "combustible principles." Some earths when heated with charcoal yielded metals. This process could be reversed, for often but not always the metal (for example, tin) on heating yielded an earthlike substance. From such an artificial earthlike substance (an oxide in modern terms) the metal could be regained if the earth was heated with charcoal. A pure earth of this sort might be called a calx, the process of forming it by heating a metal was "calcination."

How were all these facts, inherited from the Middle Ages and before, to be fitted together? By the introduction of a principle called phlogiston, closely related to Aristotle's old element, fire—closely related, yet the relationship was never clear. To those who sought for clarity it seemed evident that there must be some common principle involved in the process of making various metals from their calces and vice versa. Therefore, let us call this something phlogiston, they in effect declared. When phlogiston was added to a calx you had a metal, when you removed it from a metal a calx was formed; phlogiston was in a sense a metalizing principle. Note there is a commonsense assumption more or less implied in this line of reasoning: except for gold, and occasionally a few other metals, calces *not* metals occur in nature. Therefore, these calces were the simpler materials, something must be added to them to make them metals. Since metals were so alike, the "something" was obviously the same in all cases. We shall call it phlogiston, said Becher and his pupil Stahl in a series of books published in 1703–31.

Here was a key to unlock a maze, and it was immediately accepted. Here was a concept which provided a pattern into which a mass of otherwise unrelated phenomena could be fitted. Substances were rich or poor in phlogiston, this seemed easy to establish. What was phlogiston itself? It probably was never to be seen. Substances rich in phlogiston easily took fire and, indeed, fire was perhaps a manifestation of phlogiston, or worked with it at least. For some, fire was still an element. Charcoal was a phlogiston-rich material and on heating with a metallic calx gave up its phlogiston to the calx, making a metal. By itself charcoal burned, the phlogiston appearing as fire or combined with the air. Sulfur, using the word in its modern sense, was found free in nature; it burned when heated and yielded an acid, vitriolic acid (sulfuric acid in modern terms). Clearly, this sulfur was only vitriolic acid highly "phlogisticated"; the burning set the phlogiston free and yielded the acid.

We can write these changes in diagrammatic form to illustrate how the chemists of the eighteenth century thought:

Calx + phlogiston (from charcoal) ⟶ metal.

Metal heated in air ⟶ calx + phlogiston (to the air).

Charcoal burned yields phlogiston to the air accompanied by fire.

Phlogisticated vitriolic acid (sulfur to us) burns yielding phlogiston (to the air) + vitriolic acid (sulfuric acid).

There was one very simple flaw in all this argument and the interesting fact is that this flaw was known and talked about for fifty years before the phlogiston theory was even shaken, much less overthrown. This is a beautiful illustration of the principle in the Tactics and Strategy of Science referred to at the beginning of this section, namely, that a scientific discovery must fit the times. As early as 1630 (note the date—before Boyle was born) a Frenchman, Jean Rey, studied the calcination of tin and showed that the calx weighed more than the tin from which it was formed. More than that, he gave an explanation closely in accord with Lavoisier's ideas of 150 years later. For he said, "this increase in weight comes from the air, which in the vessel has been rendered denser, heavier, and in some measure adhesive . . . which air mixes with the calx . . . and becomes attached to its most minute particles. . . ." Boyle confirmed the increase in weight of metals in calcination in 1673 but added no support to Rey's shrewd guess (it was little more) as to the reason. In fact, if anything, he led subsequent investigators down the wrong path. At least in retrospect it seems that if he had followed up only a little more boldly his own experiments, the phlogiston theory might never have been proposed or, if proposed, never accepted seriously. Yet it is all too easy to imagine that even a still greater genius than Boyle could have discovered oxygen and revealed its role in combustion and calcination in the seventeenth century. Too much physics as well as chemistry lay under wraps which were only slowly removed by the labors of many men.

At all events, Boyle put forward the hypothesis that fire, the Aristotelian principle, had passed through the walls of the glass vessel used and combined with the metal, thereby giving it weight. This was, of course, not the same as the phlogiston theory formulated a generation later; in a sense it was the opposite because according to Boyle something was *added* to the metal in calcination, namely, fire. While in the phlogiston theory something, namely, phlogiston, was *removed*. But Bolye's writings did focus attention on the heat and flame (a characteristic of fire and calcination) rather than on the air which had figured in Rey's explanation.

A Scientific Discovery Must Fit the Times

Rey's ideas about the air seem to have been lost in the subsequent 150 years, but not the facts of calcination. That a calx weighed more than the metal was well known throughout the eighteenth century, but this fact was *not* recognized as being fatal to the phlogiston theory. Here is an important point. Does it argue for the stupidity of the experimental philosophers of the day as a few writers once would have us think? Not at all; it merely demonstrates that in complex affairs of science, one is concerned with trying to account for a variety of facts and with welding them into a conceptual scheme; one fact is not by itself sufficient to wreck the scheme. In discussing Galileo's failure and Torricelli's successful interpretation of lift pumps, I referred to the principle that a conceptual scheme is never discarded merely because of a few stubborn facts with which it cannot be reconciled; a concept is either modified or replaced by a better concept, never abandoned with nothing left to take its place.

Not only was it known in 1770 that a calx weighed more than the metal from which it was formed (which means to us that something must have been taken up in its formation), but Boyle himself back in the 1660's showed that air was necessary for fire. John Mayow and Robert Hooke at about the same date had written about burning and the respiration of animals in terms of air being "deprived of its elastic force by the breathing of animals very much in the same way as by the burning of flame." Stephen Hales, fifty years later, spoke the same language. But these men were all ahead of their times. As we reread their papers we see in spite of strange words and ill-defined ideas they had demonstrated that air in which material had been burned or animals had respired would no longer sustain fire or life; furthermore, they showed that there was an actual diminution of the volume of the air in such cases. All of which seems to force the right explanation to our eyes; not so to the chemists of the eighteenth century.

Air which would no longer support combustion had merely become so rich in phlogiston it could take up no more, the "phlogistonists" declared. Indeed, when Priestley discovered how to prepare essentially pure nitrogen, it was quite natural for him to regard it as completely "phlogisticated air," because nitrogen will not support combustion. Likewise, when he discovered how to prepare essentially pure oxygen gas by heating red oxide of mercury, he called it "dephlogisticated air." He found this gas to be like common air, though a candle burned in it more brightly than even in common air. Upon the whole, said Priestley, it may safely be concluded, "that the purest air is that which contains the least phlogiston: that air is impure (by which I mean that it is unfit for respiration, and for the purpose of supporting flame) in proportion as it contains more of that principle." This letter was read to the Royal Society on May 25, 1775. And in the same year in another letter he spoke of his newly discovered oxygen as "[an air] that is five or six times better than common air, for the purposes of respiration, inflammation and, I believe, every other use of common atmospherical air. As I think I have sufficiently proved that the fitness of air for respiration depends on its capacity to receive the *phlogiston* exhaled from the lungs this species of air may not improperly be called, *dephlogisticated air*."

Experimental Difficulties with Gases

A chemist reading the papers of the phlogistonists clutches his head in despair; he seems to be transported to an Alice-through-the-looking-glass world! But if he is patient and interested he soon recognizes that much of the difficulty stemmed from the experimenters' inability to handle and characterize different gases. This fact illustrates once again the third point of the principles outlined in the last chapter, the difficulty of experimentation. Metals and calxes, inflammable substances like sulfur, charcoal, and phosphorus, the chemists of the eighteenth century could recognize and manipulate since they were solids. Even some liquids like vitriolic acid, water, and mercury were quite definite individuals. But two gases, neither of which would support fire, like nitrogen and carbon dioxide, were often hopelessly confused; or two which burned, like hydrogen and carbon monoxide. Nearly all gases look alike except for the few which are colored. They are compressible and subject to thermal expansion to about the same degree. Their densities, i.e., the weight of a unit volume, differ but that was something not easy to determine in those days. Indeed, in the eighteenth century the distinction between weight and density (i.e., weight per unit volume) even for solids and liquids was often confused. The chemical properties of each gas are characteristic and the way each gas is prepared is different; and it was these differences that finally led to a straightening out of some of the tangled skein.

To understand the difficulties of the chemists of 175 years ago, imagine yourself an elementary student in a laboratory given glass bottles of air, of oxygen, of nitrogen, and one containing air saturated with ether vapor, and asked to tell whether or not all the "airs" or gases in the bottles are identical. The air containing the ether vapor (actually still largely air) will be the only one at first recognized as distinct. A student does not know how to proceed to examine these gases except by looking at them, smelling them, or testing their solubility in water. And from Boyle's day to Priestley's the experimenters were largely in the same predicament. They spoke of different "airs," but hardly knew whether the differences were real or due to the presence of some impurity. Thus, Priestley, writing in 1777, said:

"Van Helmont and other chymists who succeeded him, were acquainted with the property of some *vapours* to suffocate, and extinguish flame, and of others to be ignited. . . . But they had no idea that the substances (if, indeed they knew that they were *substances*, and not merely *properties*, and *affections* of bodies which produced those effects) were capable of being separately exhibited in the form of a *permanently elastic vapour* . . . . any more than the thing that constitutes *smell*. In fact they knew nothing at all of any air besides *common air*, and therefore they applied the term to no other substances whatever. . . ."

The history of the study of gases covers a hundred years from Boyle's day. A number of important improvements in techniques were made. They were brought to a focus by Priestley who in 1772 carried out extensive and very original experiments with "airs." He improved still further several techniques of handling these airs or gases which enormously simplified the experimental procedures.

Before Priestley's work only three "different airs" were known. In a few years he had discovered eleven more, including oxygen. Here is another illustration of the importance of techniques, though here we meet with an evolutionary rather than a revolutionary change.

Though Priestley was the chief figure in extending the knowledge of gases, his stubborn refusal to accept the consequences of his own discoveries has already been mentioned. It is not necessary in this chapter to discuss either Priestley or Lavoisier as individuals, though the instructor using the case history of combustion would certainly wish to do so. Nor do I propose to digress by examining the priority problems involved in the work of these two men and the Swedish chemist, Scheele, who also discovered oxygen. Such matters fall within the province of the historian of science. For the purposes of the present exposition the important questions are: Why did it take the scientists of the eighteenth century so long to get on the right road? And why were there so many stubborn travelers on the wrong road after the right one had been discovered?

The Phlogiston Theory, a Block to a New Concept

It is sometimes said that the experimenters before Lavoisier's day did not carry out quantitative experiments, that is, they did not use the balance. If they had, we are told, they would have discovered that combustion involves an increase in weight and would have rejected the phlogiston theory. This is nonsense. Rey, as I have already explained, long before the beginning of the phlogiston period showed that a calx weighed more than a metal. Quantitative experiments, though, of course, not very accurate ones, were repeatedly made. Everyone knew that a calx weighed more than the metal from which it was formed. No straightforward statement of the phlogiston theory could accommodate this fact. Yet the phlogiston theory was so useful that few if any in the mid-eighteenth century were looking to overthrow it or disprove it. Rather, they were interested in reconciling one inconvenient set of facts with what seemed from their point of view an otherwise admirable conceptual scheme. How they twisted and squirmed to accommodate the quantitative facts of calcination with the phlogiston theory makes an interesting chapter in the history of science. The eighteenth-century accounts are often confusing. Fortunately their many details need not concern the readers of this book; nor except in broad outline need they concern one teaching the principles of the Tactics and Strategy of Science with the aid of the eighteenth-century studies on combustion.

The principle which emerges is one already encountered, namely, that it takes a new conceptual scheme to cause the abandonment of an old one: when only a few facts appear to be irreconcilable with a well established conceptual scheme, the first attempt is *not* to discard the scheme but to find some way out of the difficulty and keep it. Likewise the proponents of new concepts are rarely shaken by a few alleged facts to the contrary. They seek at first to prove them wrong or to circumvent them. Thus Lavoisier persisted with his own new concept in spite of the fact that certain experiments seemed to be completely inexplicable in its terms. It was later found that the interpretation of the experiments was in error. Not so in the case of the calcination of metals: there could be no doubt in the mind of anyone by 1770 that the increase in weight during calcination was real. There was also no doubt that there should be a loss in weight according to the phlogiston theory. Or at best no change in weight if phlogiston were an imponderable substance like fire.

Attempts to Reconstruct the Phlogiston Theory

One attempt to get out of the dilemma of calcination took refuge in a confusion between weight and density (calxes are less dense than metals, but the total weight in the calcination increased). This was soon put right by clear thinking. Another attempt involved assigning a negative weight to phlogiston. This illustrates how desperately men may strive to modify an old idea to make it accord with new experiments. But in this case the modification represented not a step forward but several steps to the rear! What was gained by accommodating the quantitative aspect of calcination was lost by following the consequences of negative weight to a logical conclusion. What manner of substance or principle could phlogiston be that when it was added to another material the total mass or weight diminished? The idea that phlogiston had negative weight strained the credulity, and for the most part this logical extension of the phlogiston theory (logical in one sense, highly illogical in another) was never widely accepted. But before we laugh too hard at the investigators of the eighteenth century, let us remember that before the nineteenth century heat was considered a corporeal substance and the whole concept of the atomic and molecular theory of matter lay over the distant horizon.

To some of the chemical experimenters, the dilemma presented by the quantitative facts of calcination seems to have been accepted as just one of those things which cannot be fitted in. And this attitude is much more common in the history of science than most historians would have you believe. Indeed, it is in a way a necessary attitude at certain stages of development of any concept. The keen-minded scientist, the real genius, is the man who keeps in the forefront of his thoughts these unsolved riddles. He then is ready to relate a new discovery or a new technique to the unsolved problems. He is the pioneer, the revolutionist. And it is this combination of strategy and tactics in the hands of a master which is well worthy of study if one would try to understand science through the historical approach.

Lavoisier's Clue

To recount the history of Lavoisier's development of his new theory, and the way in which the new discoveries of the time were fitted into his scheme would mean the recital of a long story. Such an account would be out of place in this volume, though a considerable portion of it would be involved in a thorough study of the case histories at hand. Let me take a few moments of the reader's time, however, to point out how Lavoisier first seems to have taken the right turn in the road. In a famous note of 1772, he wrote as follows:

"About eight days ago I discovered that sulphur in burning, far from losing weight, on the contrary gains it; . . . it is the same with phosphorus; this increase of weight arises from a prodigious quantity of air that is fixed during the combustion and combines with the vapours.

"This discovery, which I have established by experiments that I regard as decisive, has led me to think that what is observed in the combustion of sulphur and phosphorus may well take place in the case of all substances that gain in weight by combustion and calcination: and I am persuaded that the increase in weight of metallic calces is due to the same cause. . . ."

Here we seem to see the mental process at work to which I referred a few moments ago: the perception that a new fact properly interpreted enables one to explain an old dilemma, an outstanding unsolved problem. In a sense, in this note Lavoisier outlined the whole new chemistry, as he always later claimed. (The note was deposited sealed with the Secretary of the French Academy on November 1, 1772.) To be sure, at first Lavoisier mistook the gas evolved in the reduction of a calx with charcoal (carbon dioxide, the "fixed air" of that day) with the gas absorbed in calcination. The study we can now make of his note-books as well as his later publications makes it plain that it was not until after Priestley's discovery of oxygen and Lavoisier's repetition of some of Priestley's experiments with the new gas that the nature of the gas absorbed in calcination became clear. It was only then that all the pieces of the puzzle fitted together, with the newly discovered oxygen occupying the central position in the picture. But at the outset Lavoisier recognized that something was absorbed from the air. Unconsciously he was retracing the steps Jean Rey had taken nearly 150 years earlier and which had never been followed up. Rey's almost forgotten book was called to Lavoisier's attention shortly after his first publications of his new theory.

An interesting question that will at once come to the mind of many is the following: why did the study of sulfur and phosphorus lead Lavoisier to the right type of explanation? Why after experiments with those substances did he set out full of confidence on a set of planned experiments along a new line? This is one of those historical riddles which can never be answered, but concerning which it is not entirely profitless to speculate. I suggest that the key word in Lavoisier's note of November 1, 1772, is "prodigious"—"this increase of weight arises from a prodigious quantity of air that is fixed." If this is so, we have again another illustration of how experimental difficulties or the lack of them condition the evolution of new concepts. To determine whether air is absorbed or not during the calcination of a metal is not easy; the process takes a long time, a high temperature, and both the increase in weight and the amount of oxygen absorbed are small. But with phosphorus and sulfur the experiment was relatively easy to perform (the materials burn at once on ignition with a burning glass); furthermore, the effect observed is very large. The reason for this in terms of modern chemistry is that sulfur and phosphorus have low atomic weights of 32 and 31 (oxygen is 16), and in the combustion 1 atom of phosphorus combines with 5 of oxygen; 1 atom of sulfur with 3 of oxygen. The atomic weight of the metals is high, the number of atoms of oxygen combining with them, fewer. Thus 62 weights of phosphorus will yield $62 + (5 \times 16) = 142$ parts of combustion product; while in the case of tin, the atomic weight is 118 and only 2 atoms of oxygen are involved. Thue 118 weights of tin would yield only $118 + (2 \times 16) = 150$ weights of calx or an increase of only about 25 per cent. Note that with phosphorus the increase is more than double. The corresponding differences would be reflected in the volume of oxygen absorbed, and furthermore, since the calcination of tin was a long process at a high temperature in a furnace, no entirely satisfactory way of measuring the volume of air absorbed was at hand in 1770.

Quantitative Measurements and Accidental Errors

As a matter of fact, until Lavoisier was put on the track of the gas prepared by heating mercuric oxide by Priestley, he had a hard time proving that metallic calxes did gain in weight *because* of absorption of something from the air. The method he used was to repeat certain experiments of Boyle with a slight modification. Both the modification and the difficulties are of interest and point an obvious moral to the tale. Boyle had sealed tin in a glass vessel and heated the vessel a long time on a charcoal fire (which he says is a very dangerous operation as the glass may well explode). Boyle then removed the vessel from the fire and after cooling opened the glass, reweighed the vessel and noted the increase in weight. This was one of the many well-known experiments showing that the calx weighed more than the metal. (Boyle, the reader will recall, believed the increase to be due to the fire particles which passed through the glass). Now, said Lavoisier, where Boyle went wrong was in not weighing the vessel *before* opening it. For if his explanation were right and the fire had passed through the glass and combined with the tin, the increase would have occurred before the air was admitted. While if oxygen were involved, the increase in weight would occur *after* the air was admitted. The results obtained by Lavoisier on repeating this experiment were as expected, but were far from being as striking as those obtained with phosphorus for the reasons just explained. The increase was 10 parts in a total of 4,100 in one experiment and 3 parts in about the same amount in another! We now know that the difficulties of weighing a large glass vessel with a high degree of accuracy are great, due to film moisture and electrical charges. It is, therefore, not surprising that the glass retort, after heating, varied in weight from day to day almost as much as the total gain in weight in one of the two experiments.

These tough facts of experimentation are of great importance. To me, they indicate strongly that even if Boyle had weighed his vessel before and after admitting the air, the uncertainties of his figures would probably have been so great as to confuse him and subsequent investigators. *Important advances in science are based on quantitative measurements only if the measured quantity is large as compared with possible systematic and accidental errors.* The principle of significant figures which plays so large a part in later scientific history is foreshadowed in a crude way by this episode involving the combustion of phosphorus and the calcination of tin. Therefore, in considering the case history at hand the instructor would undoubtedly wish to enlarge at some length on the whole problem of the controlled variable and the role of quantitative measurements.

Lavoisier and Priestley's Stubborn Facts

For students who had some prior knowledge of chemistry, say a good high-school course, the study of the last days of the phlogiston theory might be rewarding. For the controversy between Lavoisier and Priestley not only illustrates with what tenacity an able man may cling to a hopeless position, but also the boldness with which the innovator pushes forward. Even if a few facts appear to be to the contrary, he still pushes his new ideas just as his conservative opponent stoutly maintains his own tenets in spite of contradictory evidence. In such tugs of war which are the commonest experience in science, though usually in highly restricted areas and with limited significance, the innovator is by no means always right. This point needs to be made perfectly clear. Several case histories to this end would be worth recounting. A few dramatic instances would be in order where some bold man put forward a new idea based on alleged facts which turned out to be erroneous or erroneously interpreted.

The record of Lavoisier was the opposite. For the facts

he ignored were indeed not facts at all. Priestley's main points against Lavoisier's views were based on a mistaken identification of two different gases. This fact again emphasizes the difficulties of experimentation. Two gases, both inflammable, carbon monoxide and hydrogen, were at that period confused, even by the great experimenters with gases. Assuming their identity Priestley could ask Lavoisier to account for phenomena which were indeed inexplicable according to the new chemistry, but could be accommodated in the phlogiston theory, now being twisted more each day to conform to new discoveries. Not until long after Lavoisier's execution in 1794 was the relationship between the two gases straightened out. Therefore, Lavoisier was never able to respond to the most weighty of Priestley's arguments against his doctrine. He merely ignored the alleged facts, much as Priestley ignored the unexplained gain in weight or calcination. Each undoubtedly believed that some way would be found around the difficulty in question. Lavoisier's hopes, not Priestley's, proved well founded. So proceeds the course of science. Sometimes it turns out that difficulties with a concept or conceptual scheme are wisely ignored, sometimes unwisely. To suppose, with some who write about the "scientific method," that a scientific theory stands or falls on the issue of one experiment is to misunderstand science indeed.

A study of the overthrow of the phlogiston theory is thus seen to be more than a single case history; it is a related series of case histories. The student's knowledge of chemistry or willingness to take time to obtain this knowledge would be the limiting factor on the use of this material. Even without prior study of chemistry, I believe, a profitable excursion into this complicated bit of scientific history could be undertaken. From such an excursion would come a deeper appreciation of the two principles to which I earlier referred in this chapter. Having studied the phlogiston theory no one would fail to realize that old concepts may present barriers to the development of new ones; having traced the course of the history of experiments with gases and calcination, no one could fail to realize that scientific discoveries must fit the times if they are to be fruitful. In addition, other principles of the Tactics and Strategy of Science are constantly recurring throughout the somewhat lengthy story: the influence of new techniques, the difficulties of experimentation, the value of the controlled experiment, the evaluation of new concepts from experiment—all these are to be found illustrated more than once by those who have patience to study a strange and often neglected chapter in the history of science.

CHAPTER IV

Certain Principles of the Tactics and Strategy of Science

IN THIS chapter I shall endeavor to summarize briefly certain principles which are illustrated by the case histories presented in Chapters II and III. These are principles which have wide applicability to the development of science. It will be convenient to group them under two headings, the first corresponding to what may be called the principles of the Tactics and Strategy of Science, the other the Interaction of Science and Society.

I have ventured to define science in Chapter I as that portion of accumulative knowledge in which new concepts are continuously developing from experiment and observation and lead to further experimentation and observation. It is in that sense of the word, therefore, that the phrase, the principles of the Tactics and Strategy of Science is used. On the basis of my personal experience both as an investigator and as one privileged to follow rather closely the work of others, I feel that each of the principles listed under the first heading is exemplified almost daily in the course of the advance of science. Indeed, it is on the basis of such a conviction that these principles are set forth. For the objective of a course on Understanding Science is to convey some understanding to laymen about the way in which science is *now* advancing.

I mention this obvious point lest the necessity of drawing the case histories from the distant past leave a sense of remoteness with the reader. To repeat, the only advantage of turning to the seventeenth and eighteenth centuries for material rather than the twentieth is the relative simplicity of the factual knowledge. In the concluding portion of the college course I am proposing, the instructor would undoubtedly wish to show in a general way how the principles which had been studied in detail from the case histories of long ago are applicable to a few of the advances of the last twenty years. I have made no attempt to do this in the present volume because of the limitation of time and space.

Some readers may question my use of the words tactics and strategy in connection with the advance of science. The analogy with the military art may seem farfetched and one which in more peaceful times would be little understood by the general public. To be sure, the principles of military strategy and military tactics are principles which must be taught as such to future commanders and directors of land, air, and naval operations. The principles which I have attempted to illustrate in the foregoing chapters are rarely formulated as such by those who train our future scientific investigators. But none the less I believe they do represent the sound doctrines which have guided experimentalists in the past and are guiding them at this very moment. For the most part they are either unformulated, or else are expressed in technical language. For example, the basis of the controlled experiment and the idea of significant figures are dealt with by every one who expounds the principles of each of the separate branches of physics, chemistry, and biology. But they are bound up with a rather detailed discussion of modern laboratory procedures. In presenting these ideas to laymen a certain degree of oversimplification seems to me to be entirely justified.

Those who have some acquaintance with the two words.

—strategy and tactics—as applied to military operations may make a further objection to my usage. For I have not attempted to distinguish between the two. My reason for coupling them together is to avoid a further analysis of the details of the progress of science. Yet the analogy could be readily carried another step and an interesting and perhaps useful distinction could be made between scientists who excelled in strategy and those who were outstanding as tacticians. For example, referring to the last chapter, one may readily see the difference by comparing the work of Lavoisier and Priestley. Lavoisier's lasting contribution was made because he placed his experiments in the framework of an ambitious attempt to explain a great many facts in terms of a grand conceptual scheme. It would not be too misleading to call him a master strategist in science. Priestley on the other hand, probably excelled Lavoisier as an experimenter but he failed to appreciate fully the significance of his results in terms of the great question of the day—combustion and calcination. It is not unfair to say that he was a great tactician, but a poor strategist. Similar labels can be applied to a number of other scientific figures not without profit to an understanding of science. Perhaps, this aspect of the analogy should be developed further. At all events, by the use of the phrase Tactics and Strategy of Science, opportunity is afforded for anyone who so wishes to amplify this point.

Certain Principles of the Tactics and Strategy of Science

In the following pages a brief summary is presented of the principles which have been developed. A reference to the case history or histories illustrating each is given.

A. New Concepts Evolve from Experiments or Observations and Are Fruitful of New Experiments or Observations.

1. New concepts may result from systematic experiments or observations. This is illustrated by Boyle's development of the idea of air as a highly elastic fluid (Chapter II).

2. New concepts may result from a consideration of difficulties inherent in an old concept, the conflict between the conceptual scheme and certain stubborn facts. These facts may be well known but not yet explained. The case histories are: the limitation on the idea of nature's abhorring a vacuum implicit in the failure of the water pump to lift water more than thirty-four feet (Chapter II): the failure of the phlogiston theory to account for the increase in weight of a metal on calcination (Chapter III).

3. New concepts may result from accidental discoveries which are followed up. The case history is the work of Galvani and Volta which resulted in the invention of an electric battery (Chapter III).

4. New concepts may evolve through a series of successive approximations from older ones, the modification never being so drastic as to constitute a complete jettisoning of the older idea. In this way our modern kinetic theory of gases has grown from Boyle's first concept of air as a highly elastic fluid. Likewise, our present concepts of electricity are a growth from the ideas of Volta. Similarly, Lavoisier's explanation of combustion holds today with only slight amplifications and modifications.

5. An hypothesis or conjecture may be a limited working hypothesis such as is tested almost every day

in the laboratory in the course of a series of planned experiments. Galvani at some time must have formulated the hypothesis that the electric machine was unnecessary for the twitching of the frog's leg. On investigation this proved to be correct (Chapter III). This type of hypothesis may concern even such trivial matters as a broken wire or a bad connection invalidating an electrical experiment. We usually have no record of the incorrect working hypothesis of this sort. Their number in the course of the last three hundred years must be legion.

6. An hypothesis or conjecture may be on the grand scale in which case we may designate it a conceptual scheme. It may be fruitless and short-lived as illustrated by Galileo's explanation of the failure of water to rise more than thirty-four feet in a lift pump (Chapter II) or Galvani's concept of animal electricity (Chapter III). It may be long-lived and useful, as witness: the concept of the atmosphere of Torricelli (Chapter II), of the spring of the air of Boyle (Chapter II), of the electric current from a battery (Chapter III), of phlogiston (Chapter III), of the modern concept of combustion (Chapter III).

7. A new concept may be revolutionary and after its formulation a host of old facts may be fitted into the new scheme and many new facts discovered. Torricelli's concept of the atmosphere is an excellent example (Chapter II). Lavoisier's concept of the role of oxygen in combustion is another example (Chapter III).

8. It is important to distinguish between a new concept and the "explanation" of this concept. A good example is the contrast between Boyle's idea of

air as a highly elastic fluid and various schemes of his day which sought to explain this concept in terms of vortices or particles with spring-like qualities. In modern physics we meet the same distinctions but in a much more complicated form when discussing the electromagnetic theory of light and the concept of the ether. Since the word theory is used both for a concept and its explanation, it is an ambiguous word.

9. A scientific discovery must fit the times. The case history is Rey's discovery of the increase in weight of tin on calcination and the repeated observations of a similar nature the implications of which were largely ignored for 150 years (Chapter III).

10. A well-established concept may prove a barrier to the acceptance of a new one. If a conceptual scheme is highly satisfactory to those who use it, neither a few old facts which cannot be reconciled nor a few new ones will cause the concept to be abandoned. The case history is the persistence of the phlogiston theory as an explanation of combustion (Chapter III).

11. Old concepts may be retained in spite of alleged facts to the contrary. The case history is the last days of the phlogiston theory (Chapter III). A new concept may be pushed forward by its proponents in spite of alleged facts to the contrary. The case history is Lavoisier's failure to explain certain facts presented by Priestley, later found to be in error (Chapter III).

12. Advances in the practical arts are not the same as advances in science. No new concepts or conceptual schemes are evolved; likewise the amassing of data does not constitute advance in science.

B. SIGNIFICANT OBSERVATIONS ARE THE RESULT OF "CONTROLLED EXPERIMENTS" OR OBSERVATIONS; THE DIFFICULTIES OF EXPERIMENTATION MUST NOT BE OVERLOOKED.

1. There are always many variables in an experiment. Failure to identify the significant variables and control them within limits will vitiate the result. The case histories illustrating this point in particular are: the first measurements leading to Boyle's Law (Chapter II), the experiments of Galvani and Volta (Chapter III), and the study of the calcination of metals (Chapter III).

2. Often it is not easy to answer a simple question unambiguously by experiment. The case histories are: the attempts to establish whether or not sound was transmitted in a vacuum, and experiments to determine whether water expands in a vacuum (Chapter II).

3. Almost all experiments involve measurement. In such experiments, if the results are to have significance, the numerical values obtained must bear a certain relation to accidental variations in the numbers. The case history is the calcination of tin and the burning of sulfur and phosphorus (Chapter III).

4. Erroneous observations or interpretations of experiments frequently persist and confuse the development of new concepts. The case history is the faulty identification of carbon monoxide with hydrogen (Chapter III).

C. New Techniques Arise as a Result of Experimentation and Influence Further Experimentation.

1. New techniques of experimentation may be revolutionary. The new apparatus or procedure may represent a striking innovation and lead to many new discoveries. The case histories are: Torricelli's introduction of the use of mercury in experimentation, the invention of the barometer, the production of a vacuum (Chapter II); von Guericke and Boyle's invention of the air pump for producing a vacuum (Chapter II); Volta's invention of the electric battery (Chapter III).

2. New techniques may evolve gradually as improvements in apparatus and methods. When a certain degree of accuracy or convenience has been attained, significant new observations can be made. The case history is the handling and identification of gases (Chapter III).

3. The new technique may arise from a consideration of a practical art. The case history is the development of the air pump from water pumps of the lift or suction type (Chapter II).

4. The new technique may be developed for the purpose of exploring new phenomena: the case histories are: the improvement of the air pump by Boyle (Chapter II), and the development of techniques for handling and identifying gases by Priestley (Chapter III).

5. The new technique may arise from an accidental discovery which is followed up. This is essentially the history of the invention of the electric battery by Volta (Chapter III). A still better illustration

is afforded by a consideration of the discovery of
X rays by Roentgen (Chapter III).

The Interaction of Science and Society

The many topics which might be listed under this heading are strictly speaking not principles of the Tactics
and Strategy of Science. They represent rather certain
social phenomena which characterize the growth of science
in the last three centuries. For a college course of the type
I have been considering throughout this book, the central
topic might well be "The Growth of Science as an Organized Social Activity." With this theme in mind, the instructor could relate each case history to a developing
pattern. He would show how the early investigators of
physical, chemical, and biological phenomena were to a
large degree lone workers, and how in the middle of the
seventeenth century in different countries these amateurs
came together to form scientific societies. The role of these
societies in the subsequent years would then be traced with
particular emphasis on the expanding literature of science
and the gradual evolution of scientific investigation as a
professional occupation.

Obviously there is enormous latitude in the way this
aspect of the course might be presented and how much
time might be devoted to those phases of the case histories
which illustrate the relation of science to society. Take
the role of the universities, for example. I am inclined to
think that a study of the history of those institutions from
the sixteenth to the twentieth century is highly rewarding.

The fact that, with few exceptions, the progress of pure
science was little indebted to the work of university men
from the middle of the seventeenth century to the middle
of the nineteenth makes the story none the less significant.
This fact necessitated the setting up of various other in

stitutions for the advancement of science, and of course, greatly increased the importance of the scientific societies. Since the history of the universities is so closely inter-woven with the history of organized religion in this same period, a consideration of the academic centers of learn-ing may be useful as a focus for the discussion of the rela-tion of the development of science to religious history in several countries. Likewise, the universities would seem appropriate pegs on which to hang a discussion of epis-temological and cosmological problems. (Assuming the instructor decides to include this material.) In short, around the history of a few universities may be grouped a number of topics which relate the growth of pure science to the changing climate of opinion.

When one comes to consider the relation of pure and applied science to each other and to industry and com-merce, storm signals of present controversy are at once seen to be flying. I shall not attempt to prescribe how the instructor should balance the contending views. To my mind it is important, however, that he should point out that some modern writers have declared that "Science is the product of economic conditions of society, and its so-cial function is to benefit the ruling classes of society"; and this group have minimized any distinction between pure and applied science or between science and technol-ogy. On the other hand, such contentions have been vig-orously attacked as representing a false interpretation of history and a pernicious ideal for the future. Since the echoes of this controversy find their way into the daily press it is certainly desirable that the student be directed to the writings of the two opposing sides. In this connec-tion a reference to the application of science to medicine is of considerable importance. The interplay between theory and practice and between pure and applied science can be illustrated in this area without reference to those economic factors which have been overemphasized by some in recounting the story of the development of physics, chemistry, and technology.

The value of including other historical material drawn from the political, social, and cultural history of the last three centuries may well be questioned. In a sense it is quite irrelevant to an understanding of the principles I have outlined. Yet from a strictly pedagogic standpoint I am inclined to think that if introduced skillfully and in small quantities it would prove well worth the time required. One must bear in mind that one of the premises of my argument is that the students in question would not be future scientists, or doctors, or engineers. They would be college undergraduates primarily interested in the humanities and the social sciences. For many young people, the facts of history (as this word is usually employed) are of more lasting interest than the facts of science. Therefore, the interest of such students in the case histories could be heightened by reference to famous statesmen, soldiers, and writers who were contemporaries, and in one way or another connected with the scientists or their work. In those cases where the connection was intimate or the channels in which scientific inquiry flowed were conditioned by political events and forces, the historical setting of the case will impress itself lastingly on the student's mind.

But all good teaching depends, of course, on the teacher. I have perhaps already gone too far in laying down specifications in advance. For it was my intent merely to outline a method of approach to an important problem. No one can be a dogmatist about a course which has never yet been offered. I can only hope that a group of skillful teachers may in different colleges find some merit in my proposal. It will be for those men and women to incorporate the ideas wholly or in part as they see fit into a particular pattern of college work. Within the rather narrow limits of the material now available in translation they can choose case histories as they desire.

On every hand we see today renewed interest in experimentation with new methods of teaching science as part of a general education. This volume has been written with the hope that it may contribute in some small measure to the forwarding of this urgent task.

Notes and Bibliography

Chapter I

1. **P. 6.** Karl Pearson *The Grammar of Science* (Everyman ed), pp. 6, 13, 15. Pearson goes on to say, "I believe more will be achieved by placing instruction in pure science within the reach of all our citizens, than by any number of polytechnics devoting themselves to technical education, which does not rise above the level of manual instruction." This was written in 1892. On the whole I think few people familiar with American education today and looking at the situation relatively free from professional prejudice would subscribe to Pearson's claims as to the value of elementary science instruction. The teaching of science, that is, physics, chemistry, and biology has widely spread in our schools and colleges. Instruction in the sciences is generally admitted today to be essential (and rightly so) but the arguments for the continuation and extension and improvement of this instruction are rarely expressed in terms such as those used by Pearson in *The Grammar of Science*. Rather, elementary instruction in the sciences is usually justified by appealing to the obvious fact that a man is lost in the modern world of technology and applied science who does not have at least a rudimentary knowledge of the basic facts and principles of physics, chemistry, and biology. How these basic facts and principles are to be conveyed to high-school students is a problem. There is need for vast improvement in these areas. But this pedagogic problem, I should like to make it plain, is in my opinion different from the one to which these chapters are addressed.

The experience of fifty years does not seem to have confirmed Pearson's belief in the prime importance of instruction in *a* science as laying the basis for an improved type of citizenship. The reason for this failure of his expectations may be attributed by those who still hold to Pearson's doctrine to failure in our educational procedure.

While admitting the inadequacies of the elementary teaching in school and college in the sciences, I believe the reason goes deeper and is connected with what I feel is Pearson's failure in analyzing the processes of science and his exaggeration of the applicability of what he considers the scientific method. For example, he writes (p. 16): "The reader may perhaps feel that I am laying stress upon *method* at the expense of material content. Now this is the peculiarity of scientific method, that when once it has become a habit of mind, that mind converts *all* facts whatsoever into science. The field of science is unlimited; its material is endless, every group of natural phenomena, every phase of social life, every stage of past or present development is material for science. *The unity of all science consists alone in its method, not in its material.* The man who classifies facts of any kind whatever, who sees their mutual relation and describes their sequences, is applying the scientific method and is a man of science." My reasons for objecting to this wide use of the word science will be evident to those who continue the reading of these lectures.

2. P. 7. Lest some readers may feel that at this point and elsewhere in this book I have neglected the early development of modern astronomy on the one hand and early medical sciences on the other, let me hasten to record the well-known significance in the development of modern science of both activities. The chain of events which connects the observation of Tycho Brahe (1546–1601) with Copernicus, Kepler (1571–1630), and Newton have been presented to the public in so many forms as to be almost literally common knowledge. This is not true as regards the work of Vesalius (1514–64) and the great line of anatomists at Padua which included his pupil Fallopio (1523–62) and a subsequent holder of the anatomical chair, Fabrizio or Fabricius (1537–1619), who taught for sixty-four years and numbered among his students William Harvey (1578–1657). The publication of Harvey's great work on the circulation of the blood in 1628 is one of the landmarks in seventeenth-century science.

3. P. 9. Why and how "the wave of scientific curiosity began to mount" are, of course, among the most fascinating and difficult of historical questions. Obviously there are no simple answers. Any exposition of the "dawn of science" is certain to be in error by emphasizing unduly either one or another of a group of complex factors that were clearly at work in shaping the new era in which we live. I have heard an eminent historian of the culture of the Middle Ages declare that the humanists contributed nothing whatsoever to the beginning of modern science, in fact, their activities were probably detrimental. On the other hand, the more usual statement that the recapture of the writings and spirit of antiquity by the humanists was the determining factor in the development of science is probably an equally gross overstatement.

Galileo admittedly obtained inspiration and ideas as a young man from reading Archimedes; from this fact one can argue that the role of the revival of learning in stimulating science was great. For one can question whether a Latin translation of the Greek would have come into the hands of a man of Galileo's bent and genius three hundred years earlier. The first Latin translation of Archimedes was made by William of Moerbeke (*ca.*1215–*ca.*86) and was published by Tartaglia in 1543.

But more important than contact with the ancient world or even the increasing spread of information due to the invention of printing was perhaps the spirit of intellectual adventure so characteristic of the

Italian city republics in their days of glory. The story told of Brunelleschi (1377?–1446) by Vasari (1511–74) has always seemed to me to epitomize the boiling up of the curiosity and creative energy of the Renaissance which eventually manifested itself in scientific investigation. The story in brief is as follows: "One morning, some months after his return, Filippo was on the piazza of S. Maria del Fiore with Donato and other artists discussing antique sculptures, and Donato was relating how . . . he had made a journey to Orvieto . . . and how, in passing afterwards through Cortona, he . . . had seen a remarkable ancient marble sarcophagus, with a bas-relief, a rare thing then, . . . and so inflamed Filippo with an ardent desire to see it that, just as he was, in his mantle, hood and sabots, he left them without saying a word . . . and proceeded to Cortona led by his love and affection for art." Vasari, *The Lives of the Painters* (Everyman ed 1927), p. 276.

In this same connection Charles Singer writes, "The beginnings of effective plant study have been traced to a fortunate combination of Humanistic Learning, Renaissance Art, and the perfection of the Craft of Printing. The same is true of the study of the animal body." *A Short History of Biology* (Oxford, 1931).

4. P. 9. Science becomes a self propagating social phenomenon, according to my view, when the ferment of the Italian Renaissance spreading through each new generation of young men underwent a not-too-violent mutation; the focus of attention turned from art, archaeology, and literature to the study of the structure of plants and animals, the stars, and to mechanical contrivances (water pumps, for example, see Chapter II). If one may carry the metaphor further, this new strain of ferment was able to find a lodging in what had hitherto proved a barren medium. People less sensitive to poetry and art than the dwellers in Italian towns and cities could share the enthusiasm of those who made discoveries about the human body, or stars, or falling bodies, or ways of creating vacua. Galileo seems to me to have been a man quite in the spirit of Brunelleschi; Boyle and his friends in the Oxford of the 1650's of whom I speak in Chapter II, would have had much in common with Galileo, but I cannot imagine them transported in time and place to become boon companions of Brunelleschi. They were too near Milton in several senses of the word.

To a certain degree a new concern with practical affairs changes the focus of attention of the Renaissance man. The favorite quotation to support this view is from the opening lines of Galileo's *Two New Sciences* in which one of the interlocutors says, "The constant activity which you Venetians display in your famous arsenal suggests to the studious mind a large field for investigation, . . . all types of instruments and machines are constantly being constructed by many artisans, among whom there must be some who, partly by inherited experience and partly by their own observations, have become highly expert and clever in explanation." To which a second speaker replies, "You are quite right. Indeed, I myself, being curious by nature, frequently visit this place for the mere pleasure of observing the work of those who, on account of their superiority over other artisans, we call, 'first-rank men.' Conference with them has often helped me in the investigation of certain effects including not only those which are striking, but also those which are recondite and almost incredible." *Dialogues Concerning Two New Sciences by Galileo Galilei.* Translation by H. Crew and A. de Salvio (Evanston and Chicago, 1939), p. 1. (The book was first published in Leyden in 1638; it is Galileo's masterpiece representing more than thirty years of thought and experimentation and contains almost all his significant writings about physics. This is one of the books from which the student would be expected to read at considerable length.)

It is possible, however, to make too much of this quotation. Surely another factor in changing the emphasis for the adventurous intellect of the sixteenth and seventeenth centuries was the implications of the new astronomy. For many learned and cultural circles these two centuries were periods of deep and passionate interest in theology, and the relation of the altered cosmology to religion was dramatized by Galileo's trial. Still a third force which moved the target to a new position was the doctrine preached by Francis Bacon, and also by Descartes,—the hopeful prophecy that man would gain practical advantage by understanding and mastering the forces of nature. Bacon's dicta are well known. For a discussion of similar sentiments in France, see Harcourt Brown, "The Utilitarian Motive in the Age of Descartes," *Annals of Science,* I, (1936), 182–192.

Each one of these different elements entered into the social and cultural force which brought about the scientific age and has been described as the essential ingredient by one or more writers dealing with the seventeenth century. We have had many interesting books in the last few decades written about the interrelation of science, religion, literature, and politics in that period, particularly as to the English development. But much less has been written along comparable lines about the sixteenth century.

It is unfortunate that more material about the Italian universities of this period is not available. If we could recapture the spirit of these institutions, we would perhaps have more understanding of what may be called the prenatal history of modern science. Strangely enough, only in this period did the universities play any significant role in the birth of modern science; not till the nineteenth century do we again find the universities anywhere in the world the important centers for the advance of science.

5. P. 14. *The Grammar of Science,* p. 37. As an example of the same type of statement from another famous writer on the philosophy of science one may quote Ernst Mach: "When experience has once clearly

exhibited these facts and science has marshalled them in economic and perspicuous order, there is no doubt we shall *understand* them. For other 'understanding' than a mental mastery of facts never existed. Science does not create facts from facts, but simply *orders* known facts." The last sentence seems to give a completely false idea of the progress of science in the last hundred years unless one is to define the words emphasized in a way quite contrary to their common usage. Many of the "Facts" with which modern physics and chemistry deal might well deserve the name "artifacts"; they were not only entirely unknown to Mach writing in 1882, but would probably have seemed to him impossible. Ernst Mach, *Popular Scientific Lectures,* translated by J. J. McCormack (Chicago, 1895), p. 211. See also notes below on the nature of science.

6. P. 18. A summary of the principal topics of the course in question is afforded by the list of the principles of the Tactics and Strategy of Science with which I conclude my last chapter (p. 101). As to the importance of the controlled experiment I may strengthen my case for making a consideration of this development one of the cardinal features of the course by quoting from a recent article by P. W. Bridgman. "The first scientific epoch was initiated by what was in science a new trick of intellectual technique—the controlled experiment. This is now accepted so much as a matter of course that it requires a forceful act of imagination to recover the point of view of the early days." *Yale Review,* XXXIV (1945), 444–461. The student in the proposed course would be required to perform to the best of his or her ability just such a forceful act of imagination. And it is my contention that for a vast majority of students only by performing such an act can they hope to understand what Bridgman describes as "the development of a new tool for use by intelligence, which alone has made possible present science and technology."

In the same article the author has this to say about the scientific method. "I am not one of those who hold that there is a scientific method as such. The scientific method, as far as it is a method, is nothing more than doing one's damnedest with one's mind, no holds barred. What primarily distinguishes science from other intellectual enterprises in which the right answer has to be obtained is not the method but the subject matter."

7. P. 19. The quotation is from Ernst Mach, *History and Root of the Principle of the Conservation of Energy,* written in 1872. English translation by Jourdain (Chicago, 1911), p. 56.

"The Newtonian theory of gravitation, on its appearance, disturbed almost all investigators of nature because it was founded on an uncommon unintelligibility. People tried to reduce gravitation to pressure and impact. At the present day gravitation no longer disturbs anybody; it has become a *common* unintelligibility."

8. P. 20. "The advancement of learning in the United States in the Post-War World," *Proceedings of the American Philosophical Society,* LXXXVII (1944), 291–298.

9. P. 21. Some of the difficulties attendant on the use of the word progress are brought out in an interesting symposium on Social Progress which includes papers by L. J. Henderson, Crane Brinton, E. B. Wilson. *Proceedings of the American Academy of Arts and Sciences,* LXXIII (1940), 457–472.

10. P. 23. Quoted by Crane Brinton in his paper on "Social Progress," *loc. cit.,* p. 465.

11. P. 23. The classic on this subject is, of course, *"The Idea of Progress"* by J. B. Bury (London, 1920).

12. P. 24. To my mind there has been too little said in the popular accounts of science about both the dynamic quality of the enterprise and the fact that it is concerned with evolving conceptual schemes (rather than the classification of facts). But there is nothing new, of course, in either aspect of the definition I have just framed. Nunn in 1907 wrote, "without the implication of acceptance or rejection of the metaphysical contentions of 'Pragmatism,' we may usefully fall in with the prevailing fashion in thought so far as to replace the current static conception of Science as a body of truths by a dynamic conception of it as a definite pursuit. Such a conception of it is adopted in this essay. Science is here conceived as a definite secular creative process which may be distinguished in and traced through the conscious life of civilization." T. Percy Nunn, *The Aim and Achievements of Scientific Method: An Epistemological Essay* (London, 1907).

In the same essay the author attempts to differentiate progress in science from other human activities in terms of the motivation of the worker. This seems to me a very questionable undertaking, particularly in view of the mixed motives in regard to theoretical and practical advances in science which seemed to have prevailed in the early scientific societies. Yet the distinction between the evolution of a theoretical framework into which new observation and experiment may be placed is of prime importance. Tracing Kepler's history, Nunn writes as follows: "It will be noted that Kepler's final conception of the planetary system is *formally* less satisfactory than the earlier one—since it fails to suggest quantitative determinations by which it could be verified. At the same time it will, I hope, be agreed that when, at some moment between 1600 and 1609 Kepler, wrestling with Brahe's records, forgot his pious prepossessions in his anxiety to understand the behaviour of Mars *for the sake of understanding it,* he adopted for the first time an attitude which was genuinely 'scientific.' The *differentia* of Science, then, as a conative process whose aim is to render the Objective intelligible, is the presence of no motive except the *desire* to render it intelligible— particularly in its quantitative determination. No philosophical leanings, not even the desire of power over Nature for which Bacon was willing to be her minister, can be admitted beyond the 'margin' of the apperceptive area in which the Objective facts are central. The scientific attitude is essentially that of the *savants* who, drinking to the next great discovery, coupled with their toast the hope that it might never be of any use to anybody." *Loc. cit.*, p. 59. There is much truth in this description of the scientific attitude but it would seem that any attempt to define an activity in terms of the motives of those engaged is difficult, to say the least.

At the risk of becoming entangled in matters properly discussed only by professional philosophers, I suggest that it was Mach's failure to recognize the dynamic quality of science that led him to be so dogmatic in his anti-atomistic position. See Philipp Frank, *Between Physics and Philosophy,* chapter II (Cambridge, 1941).

The course of scientific history has decided definitely between those chemists who at the turn of the century took the atomic and molecular theory seriously and those who did not. The decision has been made not in terms of whether a conceptual scheme for the chemist with energy relations in the foreground was a more "economical representation" but in terms of which of the two viewpoints was more fruitful.

In 1872 Mach wrote the following and allowed it to stand in the 1909 edition of his essay on the "Conservation of Energy": "Now, the greater the number of atoms in a molecule, the higher the number of dimensions of space do we need to make actual all the thinkable possibilities of such combinations. This is only an example to show under what limitations we proceed when we imagine the chemical elements lying side by side in a space of three dimensions, and how a crowd of the relations of the elements can escape us thereby if we wish to represent them in a formula which cannot comprise them.

"It is clear how we can study the nature of chemical combinations without giving ourselves up to the conception mentioned, and how, indeed, people have now begun to study them. The heat of combustion generated by a combination gives us a clearer idea of the stability and manner of combination than any pictorial representation. If, then, it were possible, in any molecule composed of n parts, to determine the $\frac{n(n-1)}{1.2}$ heats of combination of every two parts, the nature of the combination would be characterized thereby. According to this view, we would have to determine $\frac{n(n-1)}{1.2}$ heats of combustion, whereas, if the molecules were thought spatially $3n - 6$ heats of combination suffice. Perhaps too, a more rational manner of writing chemical combinations can be founded on this. We would write the components in a circle, draw a line from each to each, and write on the latter the respective heat of combination . . ." (p. 53). ". . . The ultimate unintelligibilities on which science is founded must be facts, or, if they are hypotheses, must be capable of becoming facts. If the hypotheses are so chosen that their subject can never appeal to the senses and therefore also can never be tested, as is the case with the mechanical molecular theory, the investigator has done more than science, whose aim is facts, requires of him—and this work of supererogation is an evil." Ernst Mach, *"History and Root of the Principle of the Conservation of Energy,"* translated by Jourdain (Chicago, 1911; 1st German ed 1872, 2d ed 1909), p. 57. Whether today in view of the immense amount of data involving the interaction of radiation and matter which is often spoken of as "Proving the realities of atoms and molecules" Mach would still say that "the subject did not appeal to the senses and therefore can never be tested," I do not know. But surely the hypothesis has been tested from a wide variety of angles and has proved a most fruitful conceptual scheme.

Incidentally, belief in the fruitfulness (as well as the economy) of a given conceptual scheme would seem to me to provide the necessary motivation for investigators. The addition of this belief to Mach's principle of economy (and what has developed from it in recent years) would seem to answer Planck's statement that "if the Mach principle of economy were really to be put at the center of the theory of knowledge, the train of thought of such leading spirits [as the early investigators] would be disturbed, the flight of their imagination crippled, and consequently the progress of science perhaps fatefully hindered." M. Planck, *Die Einheit des Physikalischen Weltbildes* (Leipzig, 1909), quoted by Frank, *loc. cit.* I believe there is considerable truth in Planck's contention, but if the principle of fruitfulness is to be added to that of economy the force of his objection is greatly diminished. Of course, it may be contended that for nine experimentalists out of ten belief in both the economy and fruitfulness of a conceptual scheme is equivalent to belief in its reality.

When this point is reached in the discussion of the topic, in the course proposed, it will be appropriate for the instructor to call in a friend from the department of Philosophy!

13. P. 26. In connection with my definition of science and the inclusion of case material for the social sciences in the proposed course, I should like to disclaim any intent of playing the prophet as regards the future course of studies about man and society. Of course, one can arbitrarily define the word science in such a way as to exclude all the "social sciences," or include all phases of the work of social scientists. There may be merits in a definition, however, such as the one I suggest in that it focuses attention on those aspects of the natural sciences which have been most characteristic of the phenomenal growth of the last three centuries. It neither includes or excludes any of the disciplines usually classified under the heading social science. Rather it suggests that por-

tions of many if not all these disciplines may fall within the scope of the definition—and the areas thus embraced will continually widen.

If the analogy with the growth of the natural sciences be valid, those who are now social philosophers (as I have used the words) are preparing the ground for the future social scientists in a fashion comparable to the work of the early philosophers in regard to natural phenomena. Likewise, those who are concerned with social improvements—such as prison reform—and those active in accumulating knowledge and improving techniques—such as statisticians—may be paralleling in their activities those of the practical men who improved water pumps and metallurgical processes before the seventeenth century. Whether or not we have arrived at a point in the study of man where the social sciences, as I have defined the term, can effectively influence practice as physics and chemistry did technology from say 1850 on is a debatable question. Certainly there was no sharp dividing line in the history of the natural sciences between the period when practice was *not* influenced by science and the application of science dominated practice. Therefore, it seems likely that in the social sciences the transition if it occurs in a similar fashion will be equally gradual.

Bibliography

Chapter II

1. *General Works on Seventeenth Century Science and the Background to Boyle's Discoveries.*

CAJORI, FLORIAN. *A history of physics.* New York, 1938.

CREW, HENRY. *The rise of modern physics.* Baltimore, 1935.

GERLAND, E.; TRAUMÜLLER, F. *Geschichte der physikalischen Experimentierkunst.* Leipzig, 1899. Pp. 129–148, 153–162.

MACH, ERNST. *The science of mechanics.* Translated from the German by T. J. McCormack. Chicago, 1919. Pp. 110–127, 517–520.

MAGIE, W. F. *A source book in physics.* New York, 1935. Pp. 69–92.

ORNSTEIN, MARTHA. *The rôle of scientific societies in the seventeenth century.* Chicago, 1928.

PLEDGE, H. T. *Science since 1500; a short history of mathematics, physics, chemistry, biology.* London, 1939.

WOLF, A. *A history of science, technology, and philosophy in the 16th and 17th centuries.* New York, 1935

2. *The History of Pumps.*

AGRICOLA, GEORGIUS. *De re metallica. Translated from the first Latin edition of 1556 with biographical introduction, annotations and appendices upon the development of mining methods, metallurgical processes, geology, mineralogy & mining law from the earliest times to the 16th century.* By Herbert Clark Hoover and Lou Henry Hoover. London, 1912. Pumps are described in Book VI, pp. 176 ff.

USHER, A. P. *A history of mechanical inventions.* New York, 1929. Pp. 63–64, 85–94.

WESTCOTT, G. F. [Science Museum, South Kensington.] *Handbook of the collections illustrating pumping machinery.* Part 1. Historical notes. London, 1932. Pp. 34–42, 81–82. Part 2. Descriptive catalogue. London, 1933. Pp. 28–29, 167–168.

See also Wolf, pp. 512 ff.

3. *The Achievement of Galileo, Torricelli, and Their Followers.*

BRETT, G. S. "The effect of the discovery of the barometer on contemporary thought," *Journal of the Royal Astronomical Society of Canada,* XXXVIII (1944), 7–20.

GALILEI, GALILEO. *Dialogues concerning two new sciences.* Translated by Henry Crew and Alfonso De Salvio. New York, 1914. Pp. 16 ff.
The original edition is out of print, but a reprint was made in 1939, reissued in 1946, by the Editorial Board of Northwestern University Studies, Evanston and Chicago, Illinois.

LORIA, GINO, and VASSURA, GIUSEPPE (editors). *Opere de Evangelista Torricelli.* Faenza, 1919. 3 vols.
The description of the Torricellian experiment occurs in a letter written by Torricelli to Michelangelo Ricci in Rome from Florence,

June 11, 1644. Ricci's reply is dated Rome, June 18, 1644, and Torricelli's answer to Ricci's comments is dated Florence, June 28, 1644. These letters are printed in the *Opere,* III, 186–188, 189–190, 198–201. They do not mention the name of Viviani, whose name is coupled with that of Torricelli in most historians' accounts of Torricelli's discovery. Torricelli's two letters to Ricci are translated in extenso, together with the relevant portion of Ricci's reply, in *The physical treatises of Pascal* (see below under Pascal), pp. 163–170.

In Hellman's *Neudrucke von Schriften und Karten über Meteorologie und Erdmagnetismus,* Nr. 7 (Berlin, 1897), Torricelli's letters are printed under the title "Esperienza dell' argento vivo." It is there stated (p. 7) that the first printing of these letters occurred in a book without title page published in Florence, 1663, containing at the head of the first page "Lettera a filaleti di Timauro Antiate della vera storia della cicloide, e della famosissima esperienza dell' argento vivo."

Saggi di naturali esperienze fatte nell' Accademia del Cimento. Florence, 1667.

This original account of the work of the academy is also available in a translation by Richard Waller, *Essayes of natural experiments made in the Academie del Cimento.* London, 1684.

THUROT, CHARLES. "Note historique sur l'expérience de Torricelli," *Journal de physique,* I (1872), 171–176.

Extracts from Galileo and Torricelli may be found in Magie, pp. 69–73.

4. *Otto von Guericke.*

COULSON, THOMAS. "Otto von Guericke: a neglected genius," *Journal of the Franklin Institute,* CCXXXVI (1943), 241–264, 333–351.

DANNEMANN, FRIEDRICH (translator and editor). *Otto von Guericke's Neue "Magdeburgische" Versuche über den leeren Raum, (1672).* Leipzig (Ostwald's Klassiker der exacten Wissenschaften, Nr. 59), 1894.

Contains a German translation of Book III only.

VON GUERICKE, OTTO. *Experimenta nova (ut vocantur) Magdeburgica de vacuo spatio.* Amsterdam, 1672.

A portion of von Guericke's book dealing with the air pump may be found in Magie, pp. 80–84.

5. *Blaise Pascal.*

BRUNSCHVICG, LÉON; BOUTROUX, PIERRE; and GAZIER, FÉLIX. *Oeuvres de Blaise Pascal.* Paris, 1904–14. 14 vols.

LEAVENWORTH, ISABEL. *The physics of Pascal.* New York, 1930.

MAIRE, ALBERT. *Bibliographie générale des oeuvres de Blaise Pascal.* Paris, 1925–27. 4 vols.

[PASCAL, BLAISE.] *The physical treatises of Pascal. The equilibrium of liquids and The weight of the mass of the air.* Translated by I. H. B. and A. G. H. Spiers, with introduction and notes by Frederick Barry. New York (Records of Civilization, Sources and Studies, edited under the auspices of the Department of History, Columbia University, No. xxviii), 1937.
This little volume summarizing all of Pascal's "brief but brilliantly ingenious labors in natural science, together with the remarkably well-executed investigations of Perier, which completed them, was put together by Perier and published at Paris in 1663, a year after Pascal's death." In addition to this book, the editors of the present volume have included Galileo's remarks about Nature's abhorrence of a vacuum, and a translation of Torricelli's letters on the pressure of the atmosphere.

THUROT, CHARLES. "Les expériences de Pascal sur le vide et la pesanteur de l'air," *Journal de physique,* I (1872), 267–271.

Perier's letter and a selection from Pascal may be found in Magie, pp. 73–80. Also in MOULTON, F. R., and SCHIFFERS, J. *The autobiography of science.* New York, 1945. Pp. 145–153.

6. *The Life and Work of Robert Boyle.*

BARUS, CARL. *The laws of gases. Memoirs by Robert Boyle and E. H. Amagat.* New York, 1899.

FULTON, JOHN F. *A bibliography of the Honourable Robert Boyle.* Oxford, 1932. Reprinted from the *Oxford Bibliographical Society Proceedings and Papers,* III, 1–172. An *Addenda* appears in Part 3 of the same volume, pp. 339–365.

JAMES, W. S. "The discovery of the gas laws," *Science Progress,* XXIII (1928), 263–272.

MOHLER, NORA M. "The spring and weight of the air," *American Physics Teacher* (now *American Journal of Physics*), VII (1939), 380–389.

MORE, L. T. *The life and works of the Honourable Robert Boyle.* New York, 1944.

WILSON, GEORGE. *Religio chemici.* London, 1862. Essay on Robert Boyle, pp. 165–252.

7. *Work of Boyle Referred to in the Chapter.*

BOYLE, ROBERT. *New experiments physico-mechanicall, touching the spring of the air, and its effects, (made, for the most part, in a new pneumatical engine).* Oxford, 1660. (Fulton #13.)
To the second edition (Oxford, 1662. Fulton #14) was added "A defence of the authors explication of the experiments, against the objections of Franciscus Linus, and, Thomas Hobbes." The text of the third edition (London, 1682. Fulton #15) is the same as that of the second edition. The first edition is referred to as "The spring and weight of the air," the supplement in editions 2 and 3 as the "Defence." Later additions by Boyle are the "First continuation" (Fulton #16) and the "Second continuation" (Fulton #17).

The various complete works in English (#240, 5 vols., 1744; #241, 6 vols., 1772) and Latin (#242, 3 vols., 1696–97) are listed by Fulton and also various collections and epitomes (#243–#247).

The discussion of Boyle's work in this book is based largely on his "Spring and weight of the air" and "Defence."

The statement of Boyle's Law may be found in chapter v of the "Defence." Boyle acknowledges the fact that the relation between the volume and pressure of a confined gas was first suggested to him by Richard Townley and that it was independently verified by Robert Hooke, who assisted Boyle in his experiments, and also by Lord Brouncker. On the Continent this relation is known as "Mariotte's Law," although Mariotte's publication is some years later than Boyle's. Mariotte appears not to have noted the effect of temperature as Boyle did. As Wolf suggests, if it be not Boyle's Law, it is certainly Townley's rather than Mariotte's.

A good idea of the sensation created by Boyle's first publication may be had by the review of it appended to Pascal's book (see *The physical treatises of Pascal*, pp. 121–132) under the title: "New experiments made in England . . ." Whether or not this review was written by Perier, who prepared Pascal's book for publication, is not definitely known. But it was not written by Pascal himself, who died before Boyle published his work.

8. *Boyle's Controversy with Hobbes and Linus.*

BRANDT, FRITHIOF. *Thomas Hobbes' mechanical conception of nature.* Copenhagen, 1928. Pp. 377–378.

HOBBES, THOMAS. *Dialogus physicus, sive de natura aeris conjectura sumpta ab experimentis nuper Londini habitis in Collegio Greshamensi.* London, 1661. (Fulton #259.)
This is the work which aroused Boyle's ire in his "Defence."

LIARD, JOHN. *Hobbes.* London, 1934. Pp. 20, 38, 115, 117.

LINUS [HALL], F. *Tractatus de corporum inseparabilitate; in quo experimenta de vacuo, tam Torricelliana, quàm Magdeburgica, & Boyliana, examinantur, veráque eorum causâ detectâ, ostenditur, vaccuum naturaliter dare non posse.* London, 1661. (Fulton #262.)
Francis Line [or Linus], alias Hall, (1595–1675) was an English Jesuit, professor of Hebrew and mathematics at Liége. He wrote this attack on Boyle while he was a "missioner" in England. An account of him may be found in the *Dictionary of national biography,* XXXIII, 319.

SCOTT, J. F. *The mathematical work of John Wallis.* London, 1938. Chap. xi, pp. 166–172, describes the Boyle-Hobbes controversy.

Boyle's reply to the works of Hobbes and Linus is contained in his "Defence" (described above in Section 7). He returned to the attack on Hobbes (who published his *Problemata physica* in 1662) in the second of six tracts published in 1674. (Fulton #119.)

9. *The Transmission of Sound in Vacuo.*

MILLER, D. C. *Anecdotal history of the science of sound to the beginning of the 20th century.* New York, 1935. Pp. 16, 20–22.
See also Ornstein, p. 86; *Saggi* of the Accademia del Cimento, 3d series of experiments; Boyle's "Spring and weight of the air," Expt. 27, "First continuation," Expt. 41; Wolf, pp. 287–289; Gerland and Traumüller, pp. 164 ff.

Notes

Chapter II

(The following notes amplify certain of the historical matters treated in the text. However, the reader will understand that no attempt has been made to present a complete picture of the episodes in the history of science which are discussed.)

1. P. 33. *Dialogues Concerning Two New Sciences,* p. 16. The incident is related by Sagredo and the explanation agreed to by Salviati who unlike the third interlocutor Simplicio (the foil) appear throughout the discourses to represent the author's views. Salviati has just described how what he calls "the force of the vacuum" may be measured. "Whenever a cylinder of water is subjected to a pull and offers a resistance to the separation of its parts this can be attributed to no other cause than the resistance of a vacuum." He then describes a contrivance consisting of a cylinder and a tight-fitting piston carrying a hook for attaching weights: water occupies all the space between the bottom of the cylinder and the piston. The whole is inverted with the piston handle and hook pointed down, and weights are attached in increasing amount until the piston is pulled down away from the water. (So Salviati says.) In spite of the discussion about experimental difficulties which follows, one does not get the feeling that this experiment was ever really performed in a satisfactory manner. Just as Simplicio points out, what would happen with most simple contrivances would be the leaking of air into the system and the subsequent dropping of the piston for that reason. It seems doubtful to me that Galileo could have measured by his weights much more than the relative tightness of his various contrivances (assuming he actually made the experiments). The contrast of this discussion with that of Boyle written twenty-two years later on air pumps is very illuminating as showing the rapid advance in experimental science in that period.

With this brief résumé in regard to the point under discussion the quotation covering water pumps assumes its proper significance. It is as follows:

"SAGR. Thanks to this discussion, I have learned the cause of a certain effect which I have long wondered at and despaired of understanding. I once saw a cistern which had been provided with a pump under the mistaken impression that the water might thus be drawn with less effort or in greater quantity than by means of the ordinary bucket. The stock of the pump carried its sucker and valve in the upper part so that the water was lifted by attraction and not by a push as is the case with pumps in which the sucker is placed lower down. This pump worked perfectly so long as the water in the cistern stood above a certain level; but below this level the pump failed to work. When I first noticed this phenomenon I thought the machine was out of order; but the workman whom I called in to repair it told me the defect was not in the pump but in the water which had fallen too low to be raised through such a height; and he added that it was not possible, either by a pump or by any other machine working on the principle of attraction, to lift a hair's breadth above eighteen cubits; whether the pump be large or small this is the extreme limit of the lift. Up to this time I had been so thoughtless that, although I knew a rope, or rod of wood, or of iron, if sufficiently long, would break by its own weight when held by the upper end, it never occurred to me that the same thing would happen, only much more easily, to a column of water. And really is not that thing which is attracted in the pump a column of water attached at the upper end and stretched more and more until finally a point is reached where it breaks, like a rope, on account of its excessive weight?

"SALV. That is precisely the way it works; this fixed elevation of eighteen cubits is true for any quantity of water whatever, be the pump large or small or even as fine as a straw. We may therefore say that, on weighing the water contained in a tube eighteen cubits long, no matter what the diameter, we shall obtain the value of the resistance of the vacuum in a cylinder of any solid material having a bore of this same diameter. And having gone so far, let us see how easy it is to find to what length cylinders of metal, stone, wood, glass, etc., of any diameter can be elongated without breaking by their own weight.

"Take for instance a copper wire of any length and thickness; fix the upper end and to the other end attach a greater and greater load until finally the wire breaks; let the maximum load be, say, fifty pounds. Then it is clear that if fifty pounds of copper, in addition to the weight of the wire itself which may be, say, ⅛ ounce, is drawn out into wire of this same size we shall have the greatest length of this kind of wire which can sustain its own weight. Suppose the wire which breaks to be one cubit in length and ⅛ ounce in weight; then since it supports 50 lbs. in addition to its own weight, i.e., 4800 eighths-of-an-ounce, it follows that all copper wires, independent of size, can sustain themselves up to a length of 4801 cubits and no more. Since then a copper rod can sustain its own weight up to a length of 4801 cubits it follows that that part of the breaking strength [*resistenza*] which depends upon the vacuum, comparing it with the remaining factors of resistance, is equal to the weight of a rod of water, eighteen cubits long and as thick as the copper rod. If, for example, copper is nine times as heavy as water, the break-ing strength [*resistenza allo strapparsi*] of any copper rod, in so far as it depends upon the vacuum, is equal to the weight of two cubits of this same rod. By a similar method one can find the maximum length of wire or rod of any material which will just sustain its own weight, and can at the same time discover the part which the vacuum plays in its breaking strength." Reprinted by permission of the Editorial Board of Northwestern University Studies.

2. P. 35. Ornstein, *The Rôle of Scientific Societies,* p. 32.

3. P. 36. Galileo, *loc. cit.,* p. 11

4. P. 37. There can be no question that Galileo had firmly in mind the fact that air was a "ponderable medium." As in so many other matters he was one of the pioneers in the development of the new concept. (A full account of the history of this concept may be obtained from Mach's *Mechanics,* and also P. Duhem, "Le Père Marin Mersenne et la pesanteur de l'air," *Revue Générale des Sciences,* XVII, 769–782, 809–817, 1906.) Galileo describes several experiments for weighing air and gives the value of "nearly 400" as the ratio of the weight of equal volumes of water and air (*loc. cit.,* p. 80). Without the concept of air as a medium affecting bodies in a manner not unlike water (but in a very different degree) Galileo could not have handled obvious facts about falling bodies. His introduction of the idea of resistance to motion by air was crucial. It was therefore a short but decisive step that was taken by Torricelli and Viviani in 1643. Galileo it should be noted did not live to learn of these experiments by his brilliant pupils. He died in 1642 at the age of seventy-eight.

5. P. 37. In Torricelli's letter to Ricci, there are several references to "a certain philosopher" and "certain authors" and explanations as to the vacua above the barometric column. These references without further elucidation by some commentator make this letter rather unsuitable as source material for a student with an inquiring historical mind. In the letter, however, occurs the following clear statement as to the new con-cept: "We live immersed at the bottom of a sea of elemental air, which by experiment undoubtedly has weight, and so much weight that the densest air in the neighborhood of the surface of the earth weighs about one four-hundredth part of the weight of water. . . . It is often said [one wonders of whom, where, and how many months or years had passed since the first experiments] in explanation of the fact that the vessel AE [the vacuum in the top] stands empty and the quicksilver, although heavy, is sustained in the tube AC [the entire tube], that, as has been believed hitherto [this again points to the experiments having been discussed for some time], the force which prevents the quicksilver from falling down, as it would naturally do, is internal to the vessel AE, arising either from the vacuum or from some exceedingly rarefied sub-

stance; but I assert that it is external and that the force comes from without." Reprinted by permission from *A Source Book in Physics* by W. F. Magie, copyrighted, 1935, by the McGraw-Hill Book Company, Inc. I have followed Wolf, pp. 92–98, concerning the barometer.

6. P. 39. Further study may require a modification of the statement in regard to the first use of mercury for pneumatic experiments, but such use was certainly brought to the attention of the embryonic scientific world by this work. The other claims by Torricelli seem established by the frequent reference in the seventeenth century to the Torricellian vacuum and the Torricellian barometer.

7. P. 39. The route by which Pascal heard of Torricelli's work illustrates the difficulties of publication before the scientific academies and the journals were established. Perier described the spread of the news as follows: "It was the Rev. Father Mersenne of the Order of Minims in Paris, who first heard of it in France. The news was sent to him from Italy in 1644 and he in turn spread it abroad and made the experiment famous throughout the country to the admiration of all scientists. M. Pascal learned it from M. Petit, chief of the Department of Fortification, a very able scientist who had got it from Father Mersenne himself." (Pascal, *loc. cit.,* p. xvi.) Pascal was born in 1623 and therefore was a young man (25 at the time of these experiments). It may be not without significance that the new experimental philosophy, particularly the concern with air and vacua, was pushed forward in the period 1640–60 by the following who were all less than 30 at the midpoint of this period: Pascal (27), Viviani (28), Boyle (23), had Torricelli lived till 1650 he would have been 42, von Guericke was six years older. Pneumatics in the mid seventeenth century was a young man's game!

8. P. 40. I follow Wolf, p. 93, who states: "A water-barometer was constructed by Otto von Guericke, but whether independently or in imitation of Torricelli is uncertain (*Experimenta Nova,* etc., 1672). He found that it was possible, by means of an exhausted receiver, to raise water by suction from the ground level to the third story of his house, but not to the fourth story." Pascal had earlier (before 1647) likewise constructed a water barometer.

9. P. 41. Magie, pp. 80–84, gives an extract (in translation) from von Guericke's book first published in 1672 (the experiments were performed much before this date, certainly before 1654). This extract is excellent for the use of students but is very brief.

10. P. 42. The authority on the life and work of Robert Boyle is Professor John Fulton of Yale. His bibliography not only contains a bibliographical account of Boyle's major writings, but also is a mine of information concerning Boyle's achievement and the general state of seventeenth-century science.

11. P. 43. Concerning the origin of his ideas about air pumps Boyle wrote as follows:

". . . perceiving by letters from some other ingenious persons at *Paris*, that several of the Virtuosi there were very intent upon the examination of the interest of the air, in hindering the descent of the quicksilver, in the famous experiment touching a vacuum; I thought I could not comply with your desires in a more fit and seasonable manner, than by prosecuting and endeavouring to promote that noble experiment of *Torricellius; . . . .*

". . . a while before our separation in *England,* I told you of a book, that I had heard of, but not perused, published by the industrious Jesuit *Schottus;* wherein, it was said, he related how that ingenious gentleman, *Otto Gericke,* consul of *Magdeburg,* had lately practised in *Germany* a way of emptying glass vessels, by sucking out the air at the mouth of the vessel, plunged under water. . . . And though it may appear by some of those writings I sometimes shewed your Lordship, that I had been solicitous to try things upon the same ground; yet in regard this gentleman was before-hand with me in producing such considerable effects by means of the exsuction of air, I think myself obliged to acknowledge the assistance and encouragement the report of his performances hath afforded me.

". . . when the engine . . . comes to be more attentively considered, [i.e., Guericke's] there will appear two very considerable things to be desired in it. For first, the wind-pump (as somebody not improperly calls it) is so contrived, that to evacuate the vessel, there is required the continual labour of two strong men for divers hours. And next (which is an imperfection of much greater moment) the receiver, or glass to be emptied, consisting of one entire and uninterrupted globe and neck of glass; the whole engine is so made, that things cannot be conveyed into it, whereon to try experiments; so that there seems but little (if any thing) more to be expected from it, than those very few phaenomena that have been already observed by the author [i.e., Guericke] and recorded by *Schottus.* Wherefore to remedy these inconveniences, I put both Mr. *G.* and *R. Hook.* . . . to contrive some air-pump, that might not, like the other, need to be kept under water . . . and might be more easily managed"—

Quoted from *Collected Works* (London, 1772), Vol. I, "Spring and Weight of the Air," letter at beginning of book "to the Lord of Dungarvan."

12. P. 43. The Marxist interpretation of the development of science is given in its extreme form in *Science at the Crossroads* (Kniga, 1931); these essays, particularly the one by Hessen on Newton delivered at the International Congress of the History of Science in England in 1931,

appear to have influenced strongly such writers as J. G. Crowther (*Social Relations of Science,* London, 1939) and J. D. Bernal (*The Social Function of Science,* London, 1939).

The point of view presented in these books has been strongly attacked by M. Polanyi in "The Growth of Thought in Society," *Economica,* VIII (N.S., 1941), 428, and in his book *The Contempt of Freedom* (London, 1940); and by John D. Baker in *The Scientific Life* (London, 1942), and *Science and the Planned State* (London, 1945); the controversy has led to the formation of a "Society of Freedom in Science" in England.

13. P. 44. Boyle, *loc. cit.,* Expt. XVII, quoted from *Collected Works* (London, 1772), Vol. I.

"Proceed we now to the mention of that experiment, whereof the satisfactory trial was the principal fruit I promised myself from our engine, it being then sufficiently known, that in the experiment *de vacuo,* the quicksilver in the tube is wont to remain elevated, above the surface of that whereon it leans, about 27 digits. I considered, that . . . if this experiment could be tried out of the atmosphere, the quicksilver in the tube would fall down to a level with that in the vessel. . . . All things being . . . in a readiness, the sucker was drawn down; and, immediately upon the egress of a cylinder of air out of the receiver, the quicksilver in the tube did, according to expectation, subside. . . ."

Boyle's improvement over von Guericke (see Note 11) in providing a receiver into which various tubes and devices could be inserted and seen is obviously the key to this and most of his experiments. This *experimental* point should be emphasized.

14. P. 46. The quotation is from Boyle, *loc. cit.,* Expt. I. It should be noted that Descartes' doctrine (at least as presented by Boyle) is not the equivalent of the modern kinetic theory of gases, though it is nearer to it than Boyle's notion that the particles of the air each had a spring that could be bent. It was "the restless agitation of that celestial matter [something more subtle and all pervasive than air] wherein those particles [i.e., of air] swim, are so whirled round, that each corpuscle endeavors to beat off all others" . . . and later he writes, "the vehement agitation, and (as it were) brandishing motion, which they [i.e., the air particles] receive from the fluid aether, that swiftly flows between them, and whirling about each of them (independently from the rest) not only keeps those slender aërial bodies separated and stretched out (at least, as far as the neighboring ones will permit) which otherwise, by reason of their flexibleness and weight, would flag or curl . . ."

15. P. 47. On the various uses of the word *hypothesis,* Nunn (*op. cit.,* pp. 128–130) has written: "We may, it would seem, distinguish usefully between three distinct types of 'secondary construction' to all of which the name hypothesis has been indifferently given. In the first kind the *data* are a number of facts of experience which form an incomplete spatio-temporal system of a familiar type. . . . A detective's hypothesis

of a crime is of this kind. . . . In the second type of hypothesis the elements which are added to make the secondary constructions are not spatio-temporal existences but relations between such existences. Such an hypothesis was Newton's belief that the attraction of the earth for the moon could be calculated from its attraction for a stone on the earth's surface in accordance with the law of inverse squares. . . . In the last class we find the typical hypothesis of science as opposed to the hypothesis of history and common sense, the hypothesis which Ostwald has attempted to banish from scientific method. In general its marks are— (1) a lack of the homogeneity between the *data* and the added or interpolated elements which characterized the first type; (2) the *unverifiable* character of the added elements; and (3) that the secondary construction does not merely *complete* the *data* but actually replaces them. . . . The concept of molecule as used to explain physical and chemical phenomena appears to be in possession of all these marks." This was written in 1907 and shows the difficulty of applying these criteria: there are very few today who would agree that the concept of the molecule was unverifiable. On the other hand the concept of the ether as a medium for the transmission of electrical (and light) waves would be so regarded. See note, Chapter I.

16. P. 48. P. W. Bridgman, *The Logic of Modern Physics* (New York, 1927). Philipp Frank (*loc. cit.*, p. 4) has written "The misinterpretation of scientific principles, as will be shown, can be avoided if, in every statement found in books on physics or chemistry, one is careful to distinguish an experimentally testable assertion about observable facts from a proposal to represent the facts in a certain way by word or diagram. If this distinction is sharply drawn, there will no longer be any room for the interpretation of physics in favor of a spiritualistic or materialistic metaphysics."

See also "Foundations of Physics" by the same author in *International Encyclopedia of Unified Science,* Vol. I, No. 7 (Chicago, 1946).

17. P. 50. "Defence," Chapter V. An extract of this communication is given in Magie, p. 84, as is also an extract from Mariotte's work on the same subject published in 1676. Mariotte's work was independent of Boyle's and the relation between volume and pressure of a gas is often called Mariotte's Law, or the Law of Boyle and Mariotte, especially in Europe. These extracts are almost ideal for use in a course in the Tactics and Strategy of Science; indeed, a large portion of both of Boyle's books on the "spring of the air" would be suitable, though the exposition is by modern standards very long-winded and copious footnotes are required to make the matters presented intelligible to the average student.

18. Pp. 54–55. "Defence," chapter v, the whole of which is well worth reading.

19. P. 57. See Expt. XXI in Boyle's "Spring of the Air" (*Collected*

Works, London, 1772) "that the air hath a notable elastical power (whencesoever that proceeds) we have I suppose abundantly evinced— But whether or no there be in water so much as a languid one, seems hitherto to have been scarce considered, nor hath been yet, for aught I know, determined either way by any writer."

20. P. 61. On the relation of Puritanism to the development of experimental science see "Science, Technology and Society in Seventeenth Century England" by R. K. Merton, *Osiris,* IV (1938), 414–470; *Ancients and Moderns, A Study of the Background of the "Battle of Books,"* by R. F. Jones (St. Louis, 1935), and the writings on the history of science by Miss Dorothy Stimson (in particular *Bulletin, Institute of the History of Medicine,* III [May 1935], 321).

21. P. 61. An explanation of why Oxford rather than Cambridge was the center of the new experimental philosophy for a brief period has been offered by the author in a paper on "The Advancement of Learning during the Puritan Commonwealth," *Proceedings of the Massachusetts Historical Society,* LXVI (1942), pp. 3–31.

Bibliography

Chapter III

1. *The Background and History of the Work of Galvani and of Volta.*

GLIOZZI, MARIO. *L'elettrologia fino al Volta.* Naples, n.d. (preface dated 1937). 2 vols.
Chapter xvi is devoted to Galvani, chapter xvii to Volta.

HOFF, HEBBEL E. "Galvani and the pre-Galvanian electrophysiologists," *Annals of Science,* I (1936), 157–172.

MOTTELAY, PAUL FLEURY. *Bibliographical history of electricity and magnetism chronologically arranged.* London, 1922.

POTAMIAN, BROTHER; WALSH, JAMES J. *Makers of electricity.* New York, 1909.
Contains a chapter on Galvani and one on Volta.

ROSENBERGER, FERD. *Die moderne Entwicklung der elektrischen Principien.* Leipzig, 1898.

WALKER, W. CAMERON. "The detection and estimation of electric charges in the eighteenth century," *Annals of Science*, I (1936), 66–100.

WALKER, W. CAMERON. "Animal electricity before Galvani," *Annals of Science*, II (1937), 84–113.

WHITTAKER, E. T. *A history of the theories of aether and electricity from the age of Descartes to the close of the nineteenth century*. London and Dublin, 1910.
Chapter III is devoted to a history of Galvanism.

WOLF, A. *A history of science, technology, and philosophy in the eighteenth century*. New York, 1939.

2. *The Writings of Galvani and Volta.*

FULTON, JOHN F., and CUSHING, HARVEY. "A bibliographical study of the Galvani and the Aldini writings on animal electricity," *Annals of Science*, I (1936), 239–268.

GALVANI, LUIGI. *De viribus electricitatis in motu musculari commentarius*. Bologna, 1791.
This work was published in 1791 "as one of the 'Opuscula' in the proceedings of the Bologna Academy, i.e., *De Bononiensi scientiarum et artium instituto atque academia*," 1791, VII, 363–418. It was issued separately in two printings in the same year. In the Fulton-Cushing bibliography, one can find bibliographical descriptions of the many Latin editions, the two German translations, and the extract translated into Italian. Short portions of this classic have been translated into English and appear in Magie and Potamian-Walsh. An English translation and facsimile edition is at present being prepared for publication by Helen Lewis Thomas and I. Bernard Cohen, and will be published by the Burndy Library, New York City.

SARTON, GEORGE. "The discovery of the electric cell (1800)," *Isis*, XV (1931), 124 ff.
Contains a facsimile reprint of Volta's paper with comments.

VOLTA, ALESSANDRO. "On the electricity excited by the mere contact of conducting substances of different kinds," *Philosophical Transactions* (1800), pp. 403–431.
This is Volta's classic memoir, in which he describes the construction

and operation of the battery. The original is in the form of a letter to Sir Joseph Banks, President of the Royal Society of London. An excellent translation of this important document has been made by E. C. Watson and appears in the *American Journal of Physics*, XII (1945), 397–406.

Short extracts from both Galvani's and Volta's works appear in Magie, *A Source book in physics*. New York, 1935. Pp. 420–431.

3. *Roentgen and the Discovery of X rays; N rays.*

BARKER, GEORGE F., translator and editor. *Röntgen rays, memoirs by Röntgen, Stokes, and J. J. Thomson.* New York, 1899.

GLASSER, OTTO. *Wilhelm Conrad Röntgen and the early history of the roentgen rays.* Springfield, Ill., 1934.

SEABROOK, WILLIAM. *Doctor Wood.* New York, 1941. Pp. 233–240 describe R. A. Wood's exposure of Blondlot's N rays. See also *Nature,* LXX (1904), 530.

4. *The Background of the Phlogiston Theory.*

HOLMYARD, E. J. "Chemistry to the time of Dalton." London, 1925. Chapters in the *History of science,* III.

HOLMYARD, E. J. *Makers of chemistry.* Oxford, 1931.

KOPP, H. *Geschichte der Chemie.* Braunschweig, 1843–47. Reprinted, Leipzig, 1931. 4 vols.

LOWRY, T. M. *Historical introduction to chemistry.* 3d ed. London, 1936.

McKIE, DOUGLAS. "The Hon. Robert Boyle's Essay of Effluviums," *Science Progress,* XXIX (1934), 253 ff.

McKIE, D. "Chérubin D'Orléans: a critic of Boyle," *Science Progress,* XXXI (1936), 55 ff.

METZGER, HÉLÈNE. *Les doctrines chimiques en France.* Paris, 1923.

METZGER, H. *Newton, Stahl, Boerhaave et la doctrine chimique.* Paris, 1930.

PARTINGTON, J. R. *A short history of chemistry.* London, 1939.

PARTINGTON, J. R. and McKIE, DOUGLAS. "Historical studies on the phlogiston theory. I. The levity of phlogiston," *Annals of Science,* II (1937), 361–404; "II. The negative weight of phlogiston," *ibid.,* III (1938, 1–58. "III. Light and heat in combustion," *ibid.,* III (1938), 337–371. "IV. Last phases of the theory," *ibid.,* IV (1939), 113–149.

VON MEYER, ERNST. *A history of chemistry from earliest times to the present day.* Translated by George McGowan. 3d ed. London, 1906.

WHITE, J. H. *The history of the phlogiston theory.* London, 1932.

5. *The Work of Lavoisier and Priestley.*

AYKROYD, W. R. *Three philosophers (Lavoisier, Priestley, and Cavendish).* London, 1935.

BERTHELOT, M. *La révolution chimique; Lavoisier.* Paris, 1890.

COCHRANE, J. A. *Lavoisier.* London, 1931.

GRIMAUX, ÉDOUARD. *Lavoisier, d'après sa correspondence, ses manuscrits, ses papiers de famille et d'autres documents inédits.* 2d ed. Paris, 1896.

HARTOG, Sir PHILIP J. "The newer views of Priestley and Lavoisier," *Annals of Science,* V (1941), 1–56.

HARTOG, Sir PHILIP. "Joseph Priestley and his place in the history of science," *Proceedings of the Royal Institution of Great Britain* (1931), pp. 1–36.

HOLT, ANNE. *A life of Joseph Priestley.* London, 1931. With an introduction by F. W. Hirst.

McKIE, DOUGLAS. *Antoine Lavoisier, the father of modern chemistry.* London, 1935.

MELDRUM, ANDREW NORMAN. *The eighteenth century revolution in science—the first phase.* London, 1929.

METZGER, HÉLÈNE. *La philosophie de la matière chez Lavoisier.* Paris (Actualités scientifiques et industrielles, 218), 1935.

MIELI, ALDO. *Lavoisier y la formación de la teoría química moderna.* Buenos Aires, 1944.

SMITH, EDGAR F. *Priestley in America.* Philadelphia, 1920.

SPETER, MAX. *Lavoisier und seine Vorläufer.* Stuttgart, 1910.

6. *Writings of Lavoisier and Priestley.*

FULTON, JOHN F. and PETERS, CHARLOTTE H. *Works of Joseph Priestley, 1733–1804, preliminary short title list.* New Haven, 1937.

LAVOISIER, ANTOINE LAURENT. *Oeuvres.* Paris, 1862–93. 6 vols.

LAVOISIER, A. L. *Elements of chemistry.* Translated by Robert Kerr. 1st ed. Edinburgh, 1790; 4th ed. Edinburgh, 1802. A facsimile edition of this translation is available from Edwards Brothers, Ann Arbor, Michigan.

PRIESTLEY, JOSEPH. *Experiments and observations on different kinds of air.* London, 3 vols., 1774, 1775, and 1777. *Experiments and observations relating to various branches of natural philosophy; with a continuation of the observations on air.* Vol. 1, London 1779, and Vols. II and III, Birmingham, 1781 and 1786.

Notes

Chapter III

1. P. 66. Luigi Galvani (1737–98), Professor of Medicine at Bologna.
2. P. 67. Swammeradam's statement may be found in Potamian-Walsh, p. 144.
3. P. 67. The quotations are from Galvani's memoir. All of this paper should be read by the student of this case history. I have omitted the steps by which Galvani first discovered that two different metals were essential. In his own words they were as follows:

" . . . as I had casually noticed that the prepared frogs, which were hung by a brass hook passing through the spinal cord to the iron grating which enclosed a hanging garden of our house, showed the usual contractions not only when there was lightning but also when the sky was clear and fair, I thought that the origin of these contractions might be found in the changes which nevertheless were going on in the atmospheric electricity. . . . Thus I observed at different hours and indeed for days at a time suitably arranged animals, but scarcely ever did a motion of the muscles occur. Finally, tired of this useless waiting, I began to squeeze and press the hooks which were fastened in the spinal cord against the iron grating, in order to see whether such an artifice might excite the contraction of the muscles and whether instead of its depending on the condition of the atmosphere and its electricity any other change and alteration might have an influence. I quite often observed contractions, but none which depended upon the different conditions of the atmosphere and its electricity.

"As I had observed these contractions only in the open air . . . there seemed to be little lacking to my argument and I might have referred such contractions to the atmospheric electricity which enters the animal and accumulates there and suddenly leaves it when the hook is brought in contact with the iron grating. *So easy is it to deceive oneself in experimenting, and to think that we have seen and found that which we wish to see and find.* (Italics mine. J. B. C.)

"But when I transferred the animal to a closed room, had laid it on an iron plate, and begun to press the hook which was in the spinal cord against the plate, behold, the same contractions, the same motions! I repeated the experiment by using other metals at other places and on other hours and days; with the same result, only that the contractions were different when different metals were used, being more lively for some and more sluggish for the others." Reprinted by permission from *A Source Book in Physics* by W. F. Magie, copyrighted, 1935, by the McGraw-Hill Book Company, Inc.

4. P. 68. On the use of the word hypothesis, see note, Chapter II. The phrase "working hypothesis" seems to me a useful one and sufficiently definite to avoid some of the difficulties often encountered with the words hypothesis or theory. A "working hypothesis" is little more than the common-sense procedure used by all of us every day. Encountering certain facts, certain alternative explanations come to mind and we proceed to test them. Nowadays this is done by millions of people in connection with complex situations involving mechanics and electricity. The procedure of the electrician (or the handy husband) determining which fuse is blown out is exactly the procedure of the experimental scientist during a large fraction of his profitable working hours. It is also a procedure which must have been instructive for the cave man in certain situations or he would never have survived. There

is a difference in degree amounting to one in kind between the use of the working hypothesis and the construction of a new conceptual scheme (also often called an hypothesis at first). A conceptual scheme (such as the idea of the atmosphere as something exerting pressure on water causing it to rise) may be considered an hypothesis on a grand scale. If the hypothesis proves fruitful it may be given the name theory or be accepted as a "fact." I have avoided the use of the word theory except where it has become an accepted part of the language of science as "kinetic theory of gases" and the "phlogiston theory." The words concept and conceptual scheme seem to me much preferable to the use of the words hypothesis and theory.

The point is referred to again in Chapter IV.

5. P. 70. The quotation from Volta is from his letter of March 20, 1800, to Sir Joseph Banks.

6. P. 72. The controversy between Galvani's pupils and Volta was carried on largely by Aldini, the nephew of Galvani. A full account of his activities may be found in the Fulton-Cushing bibliography.

7. P. 73. Wilhelm Konrad Roentgen (1845–1923). Professor of Würzburg at the time of his famous experiment; later Professor of Physics at Munich. The announcement of his discovery was made in a paper entitled "Ueber eine neue Art von Strahlen" *Sitzungsberichte der Würzburger Physikalischen-Medicinischen Gesellschaft,* December, 1895. If this case history is used, the instructor should also consider giving an account of the announcement of N rays and the subsequent disproof of their existence. The false leads in science are rarely recorded or examined; but their study can lead to much information about the principles of the Tactics and Strategy of Science.

8. P. 73. The invention of the electric battery like that of the Torricellian barometer and the air pump had tremendous scientific repercussions. Sometimes we use the word invention only to describe a new creation which either has practical utility or is intended to have practical utility in connection with manufacturing or commerce or agriculture or the practice of medicine. A digression might be in order at some point in a course on the Tactics and Strategy of Science on the differences and similarities between scientific discovery, scientific invention, and practical inventions. The lines are never sharp. There is, however, a great difference between a new instrument or device developed as a consequence of new experiments and new concepts, and one which is an empirical change of a not well-understood contrivance or process. This difference corresponds to the difference between progress in science and progress in the practical arts. It is of much greater significance than any difference arising from the use or the proposed use of the new device. There are, of course, plenty of border-line cases, particularly in the history of the invention of electrical equipment in the second half of the nineteenth century.

9. P. 75. *The following Summary of Certain Facts about Combustion and Calcination in Terms of Modern Concepts* may be of value to some readers.

1. Air is a mixture of gases principally composed of oxygen and nitrogen; it also contains water vapor and small amounts of carbon dioxide and certain rare gases.

2. When a substance burns in air, a chemical reaction takes place involving oxygen. Most common combustible materials contain carbon compounds and when these substances burn, the carbon ends up as carbon dioxide, the hydrogen of the combustible material as water. Energy is evolved in the process as heat and light. (Gunpowder and a few other materials "burn" without the intervention of oxygen in the air; they represent mixtures of chemicals ready to undergo a reaction with the evolution of energy once they are "touched off.")

3. When most metals are heated in air they combine with oxygen to form nonmetallic substances known as oxides. (The same process occurs slowly at room temperature as, for example, the rusting of iron.) This process is often called calcination since the older term for an oxide was calx.

4. When the oxide of many metals either formed as in 3, or as found in nature in the rocks, is heated with carbon (charcoal or coke) the oxygen combines with the carbon forming an oxide of carbon, a gas, and leaving the metal behind. This is the essence of the smelting of ore known as an empirical art for ages.

5. Substances which combine with oxygen when heated with a confined volume of air use up the oxygen; the residue (largely nitrogen) will no longer support combustion or the respiration of animals.

10. P. 80. As to the slow acceptance of Lavoisier's ideas, see White, chapter XII and in particular Partington and McKie, IV, from which the following is taken. A German chemist writing in 1788 about the adherents to Lavoisier's doctrines (then still few) said:

"They by no means reject the principle of combustibility [i.e., phlogiston] from conviction, but rather, from obstinacy and love of novelty, they will not find it everywhere where others found it; and in order to introduce an entirely new language into the explanation of chemical phenomena they must displace at least the name of phlogiston, without which name nothing fundamental can be said about hardly any body according to the old teaching." By 1796, however, another German could write:

"As for our Germany, the chemical revolution has taken effect," and "this country no more counts among its chemical authors any partisan of the traditional phlogiston system, since I have convinced them of the presence of oxygen in oxide of mercury heated to redness by fire." Quoted in Partington and McKie, II, *loc. cit.,* p. 57.

11. P. 80. On the effectiveness of the phlogiston theory as a conceptual scheme and the early history, see White, chapters I–VII.

12. P. 84. Meldrum, *loc. cit.*, p. 4, writes: "The salient facts were available to all chemists. It had long been known that air has weight; that a metal increases in weight when it is calcined." On the relation of Rey's work to Lavoisier, Meldrum, p. 44.

13. P. 84. John Mayow (1645–79), a physician who wrote of "nitro-aerial particles" in air. His speculative concept while on the right track was not reinforced by appropriate experiments. Robert Hooke (1653–1783) a co-worker of Boyle's and also an important investigator in his own right. Both men recognized that the air plays an important part in combustion. White, pp. 19–21.

Stephen Hales (1677–1761), Vicar of Teddington. The most important contributions to the physiology of plants and animals in connection with the movement of water and plants. He is best known for his *Vegetable Staticks,* printed in 1727 in which appears the statement:

"It is well known that air is a pure elastic fluid, with particles of very different natures floating in it, whereby it is admirably fitted by the great Author to be the breath of life, of vegetables as well as animals, without which they can no more live nor thrive than animals can." White, p. 28.

14. Pp. 84–85. The principle that a scientific discovery must fit the times can be illustrated by many examples but none more strikingly perhaps than those given in connection with the history of the phlogiston theory. A number of the arguments of later-day historians about priority of discovery reveal the recurrence of this principle in the history of science. If science is a progressive development of conceptual schemes arising from experiment and observation and leading to new experiments and observations, a scientific discovery might just as well not have been made if it is not incorporated into the growing fabric. Similarly, new concepts which are not taken up and used are of no significance. Yet the unearthing of the historical facts about such discoveries and ideas are of importance to one interested in the Tactics and Strategy of Science, for such instances provide the case material so necessary to understand this important principle.

15. P. 85. On the importance of Priestley's work as an experimenter, see the review by Hartog, *loc. cit.*, which gives many references to other recent historical papers on the subject. Also McKie's *Lavoisier,* chapter v. The development of the "pneumatic trough" (a device for collecting gases and storing them over water or mercury) and the use of large burning glasses for heating material enclosed in glass containers has never been adequately treated by historians of science. Yet on the improvements in the manipulation of gases and reactions in gases depended the progress of chemistry in the eighteenth century. The significance of

new and improved techniques in the development of science is once again emphasized by a consideration of this subject.

16. P. 85. For the use and abuse of the phlogiston theory see White and articles by Partington and McKie.

17. Pp. 85, 87. Quotations taken from Meldrum, p. 49, Hartog, p. 23, Lowry, chapter v, b.

18. P. 90. On the negative weight of phlogiston see Partington and McKie, *loc. cit.*, II.

19. P. 91. On the evaluation of Lavoisier's thought and the relation of his work to Priestley see Meldrum, *loc. cit.*, whom I have followed in general and from whom I have taken the quotations. See also Hartog, *loc. cit.*

20. P. 94. The figures quoted are given in Meldrum. The interpretation as far as the difficulties of experimentation are concerned and their possible significance is mine. McKie's article on Chérubin D'Orléans is of importance in this connection. He emphasizes the fact that Boyle in a letter published in his collected works discusses the possibility that the increase in weight could occur by absorption of the air. But Boyle states, "I remember I did weigh a sealed retort, with matter in it, and found it encreased in weight." This malobservation (to use McKie's phrase) seemed to prove that air was not involved. The error resulted from the difficulties of measuring small changes in weight which occurred in this experiment.

21. P. 95. To conclude the story of the chemical revolution we should record that in 1787 Lavoisier and several colleagues read a paper to the French Academy on a new nomenclature in chemistry; in 1789 Lavoisier's book on the *Elements of Chemistry (Traité élémentaire de chimie)* appeared. In the latter is summed up not only the chemical revolution of the previous decade, but its wide consequences for chemistry in general. From this period stem the first comprehensive ideas of element and compound and the insistence on the significance of what is now called the material balance in a chemical reaction and the importance of the quantitative analysis of materials.

22. P. 96. Readers with some knowledge of chemistry may be interested in more details concerning the controversy between Priestley and Lavoisier which turned on a confusion between carbon monoxide and hydrogen. Hydrogen, called inflammable air (prepared in the 1760's by Cavendish by the action of acids on metals) was at first thought to be phlogiston itself since it was a gaseous inflammable material. But when Priestley discovered that the explosion of this gas with oxygen ("dephlogisticated air" to him) yielded water and this was established by Cavendish's thorough work, inflammable air became "phlogisticated water." (Either as phlogiston or phlogiston plus water it should transform a calx into a metal, according to the classical phlogiston theory.

Of course it did, but as Lavoisier pointed out, the calx was diminished in weight in the process because, as he said, oxygen was taken away from it, not phlogiston added.) Now it so happened that when carbon monoxide was discovered in 1776, this substance became thoroughly confused with hydrogen; they were both considered to be the same "inflammable air." Therefore, when Priestley said in 1786 that Lavoisier could not explain why "inflammable air" was obtained either from charcoal by heating in a vacuum with a burning glass or by heating steam with a metal, he was right. For the two inflammable gases were in fact totally different! Yet see how nicely this error fitted the book of those who were fighting a rear-guard action in defense of phlogiston. Charcoal was rich in phlogiston, they said, so on heating it in vacuo, phlogiston came off either by itself or united with water (the explanation here seemed to vary), that is, an inflammable air was formed. And since this same air (so it was thought) formed water when burned with "dephlogisticated air," why water naturally could be phlogisticated still more when heated with a metal, thereby forming the dephlogisticated metal or a calx. It is remarkable how, when you once get hold of the wrong end of even a scientific stick, you cannot let it go.

Priestley's challenge to Lavoisier may be summarized as follows:

Charcoal plus heat yielded inflammable air. Metal plus steam yielded inflammable air plus calx. If inflammable air was phlogiston plus water since both charcoal and metal contained phlogiston this was as it should be (some water would be present in the charcoal too). If the two inflammable airs are the same (which no one then questioned) how could their formation be explained without the idea of phlogiston? In modern times the facts were actually as follows: Charcoal heated yielded carbon monoxide (a small amount of oxygen was always present), iron and steam yielded hydrogen plus iron oxide.

Index

THE TERRY LECTURES

Volumes Published by the Yale University Press
on the Dwight Harrington Terry Foundation